SCHOLASTIC

Handling SCIENCE Data

T S. EVA

Activities to develop information-processing skills

YEAR **4** Scottish Primary 5

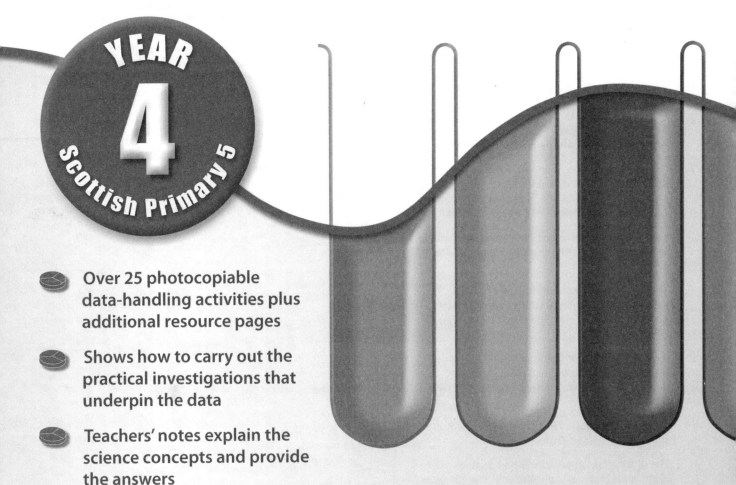

- Over 25 photocopiable data-handling activities plus additional resource pages

- Shows how to carry out the practical investigations that underpin the data

- Teachers' notes explain the science concepts and provide the answers

- Ideal for SATs practice

Peter Harwood and Joyce Porter

Authors
Peter Harwood
Joyce Porter

Editor
Joel Lane

Assistant editor
David Sandford

Series designer
Anna Oliwa

Designer
Erik Ivens

Cover illustration
Edward Eaves

Illustrations
Ann Kronheimer

Text © Peter Harwood and Joyce Porter 2002
© 2002 Scholastic Ltd

Designed using Adobe Pagemaker

Published by Scholastic Ltd,
Villiers House,
Clarendon Avenue,
Leamington Spa,
Warwickshire CV32 5PR

Printed by Bell & Bain Ltd, Glasgow

6 7 8 9 0   8 9 0 1

British Library Cataloguing-in-Publication Data
A catalogue record for this book is available
from the British Library.

ISBN 978-0590-53766-7

Visit our website at www.scholastic.co.uk

Acknowledgements
The authors and publishers wish to thank:

AstraZeneca Science Teaching Trust for their funding
and support of the research project on which the
activities in this book are based (you can visit the
AZSTT website at www.azteachscience.co.uk).

The children of Knowsley, Powys and Trafford LEAs
for their help in testing these investigations in the
classroom.

The National Curriculum for England 2000
© The Queens Printer and Controller of HMSO.
Reproduced under the terms of HMSO Guidance
Note 8.

A Scheme of Work for Key Stages 1 and 2: Science
© Qualifications and Curriculum Authority.
Reproduced under the terms of HMSO Guidance
Note 8.

The graphs on page 23 are based on information
supplied by the Met Office.

The illustration on page 62 is based on an
illustration previously published in *The Education
Guardian* on April 16th 1991.

CONTENTS

PAGE NO.	ACTIVITY TITLE	GRAPH TYPE	SCIENCE CURRICULUM REFERENCES		
			QCA UNIT	NATIONAL CURRICULUM	SCOTTISH 5-14
10	Pond life jigsaw	Flow diagram	4B	Sc2: 4b,c, 5a, b, d, e , f	Variety and characteristic features B; Interaction of living things with their environment B
12	Minibeast safari	Bar graph	4B	Sc2: 5a, b, c	Variety and characteristic features B; Interaction of living things with their environment A, D
14	Little game hunt	Pictogram	4B	Sc2: 5a, b, c	Variety and characteristic features B; Interaction of living things with their environment A
16	What plants grow in our lawn?	Bar graph	4B	Sc2: 5a, b	Interaction of living things with their environment A, C, D
18	Keys	Branched key	4B	Sc2: 4a, b	Variety and characteristic features C
20	Growing up	Bar graph	4A	Sc2: 1a, 2f	The processes of life B
22	How do we grow?	Bar graph	4A	Sc2: 1a, 2f	The processes of life B
24	Using muscles	Bar graph	4A	Sc2: 2d	Variety and characteristic features A; Forces and their effects B
26	Ice pops	Diagram	4C	Sc3: 1b, 2c	Materials from Earth A, B
28	Keeping warm	Bar graph	4C	Sc3: 1b, 2c	Materials from Earth B; Properties and uses of energy D
30	How hot is it?	Bar graph	4C	Sc3: 2c	Properties and uses of energy B, D
32	Looking at the weather	Bar graph	4C	Sc1: 2i, j; Sc3: 2c	Earth in space B
34	Keeping your lolly cold	Line graph	4C	Sc3: 1b, 2c	Materials from Earth B; Properties and uses of energy D
36	Keeping baked potatoes hot	Line graph	4C	Sc3: 1a, b, 2c	Materials from Earth B
38	Classifying materials	Table of data	4D	Sc3: 1e	Materials from Earth C
40	Thick and thin liquids	Bar graph	4D	Sc3: 1e	Materials from Earth C
42	Dissolving sugar	Bar graph	4D	Sc3: 2a, 3b	Changing materials B
44	Car ramps	Table of data	4E	Sc4: 2c	Forces and their effects A, B, C, D
46	A heavy box	Bar graph	4E	Sc4: 2c, e	Forces and their effects A, B, C
48	Friction on different surfaces	Bar graph	4E	Sc4: 2c, e	Forces and their effects B, C
50	Parachutes	Bar graph	4E	Sc4: 2c	Forces and their effects B, C
52	Boats in the gutter	Bar graph	4E	Sc4: 2c	Forces and their effects C, D
54	Why is swimming difficult?	Bar graph	4E	Sc4: 2c	Forces and their effects C
56	Strike a light	Circuit diagram	4F	Sc3: 1c; Sc4: 1a, b	Properties and uses of energy A, C; Materials from Earth A, B
58	Adding batteries	Circuit diagram, bar graph	4F	Sc4: 1a, b	Properties and uses of energy C, D; Conversion and transfer of energy C
60	Adding bulbs	Bar graph	4F	Sc4: 1a, b	Properties and uses of energy C, D; Conversion and transfer of energy C

INTRODUCTION

WHY HAVE BOOKS ABOUT HANDLING DATA FOR SCIENCE?

Children's education should provide them with skills that will benefit them for years to come. Against this background, children's ability to read and interpret information from graphs and charts is not only essential in science, but also for in everyday life, where children are exposed to information on television, in newspapers and in magazines.

In the early days of the National Curriculum, the APU[1] examined graph work in school science. They found that children could successfully carry out many of the basic skills involved in drawing graphs and reading information from graphs. However, most of the children failed to look for and describe patterns in their data, and did not understand the wider applications of graphs. The AKSIS project[2] revisited the use and application of graphs in school science. In their research, they found *'that over 75% of pupils' graphs were incorrectly constructed and most pupils regarded graphs as an end in themselves.'* One of the aims of the project was *'that Scientific Enquiry should develop pupils' understanding of the nature of scientific activity and the relation between data and scientific theories.'*

More recently, the OFSTED subject report on Primary Science (1999–2000) concluded that *'science skills, such as handling data, that draw upon and develop numeracy need to be improved systematically. Pupils are given sufficient opportunity to develop their science through practical activities. However their ability to interpret their results and say what they have found out is sometimes hampered by their lack of understanding of charts and graphs and lack of practice in recognising patterns in data. When they are encouraged to draw their own conclusions and are helped in this by discussion with the teacher, they show better understanding of the science and can apply it in different circumstances.'*

HOW THESE BOOKS HELP

This series of books is timely, then. They have been produced to help children develop their skills in handling data and its interpretation in science. However, these activities came about initially not from a response to OFSTED, but out of a need expressed by teachers. We have been undertaking a four-year research programme, 'Developing Excellence in Primary Science', generously funded by the AstraZeneca Science Teaching Trust. This project has involved working with a wide variety of children and teachers. It was not simply an academic research project; it was soundly based in the classroom, with real teachers and real children in real teaching situations.

The research team comprised a group of experienced practitioners in class teaching, and advisory and academic research, who have worked closely with teachers to address the difficulties of trying to teach science effectively. Working with primary children, alongside their teachers, clearly showed us that there was a need to develop children's data-handling skills in situations that the children were not familiar with. There is a strong tendency for primary children to learn science in a specific context, which can then make it difficult for them to apply their new knowledge to other situations. On seeing a data-handling exercise, children would often respond, 'I haven't done this' – referring to the context, which was not significant to simply interpreting the data.

An analysis of children's performance in the Key Stage 2 National Tests[3] concurs with the OFSTED report. It shows clearly that children have considerably more difficulty applying their knowledge to new situations (a problem of contextualised learning) and of *describing* trends in an acceptable scientific format although, on further questioning, the children had an underlying ability to identify trends in data. In this series, both of these aspects of interpretation are addressed and advice is given to help you develop these skills with your class.

The activities in *Handling Science Data* aim to highlight and provide opportunities to develop those skills that are common to data-handling, as well as showing the children activities that have a practical basis, which are

similar, but not necessarily identical, to some they have already done. This should help them to develop the confidence to tackle new scenarios and look primarily at the data itself.

The essential ability to analyse scientific evidence, as highlighted in the Reports, and the ability to be able to express these ideas scientifically has also been addressed. These are typically the '–er, –er' answers in National Test papers, for example 'the larger the force, the bigger the stretch'. Examples that the children can practise with are given in several of the activities. While children can often recognise the trend in the data mentally, they find it difficult to express their ideas in a concise and complete way: a common response would be, for example, 'It gets bigger' (for an elastic material being stretched), or the children may give very roundabout descriptions from which the you might have to extract the trend. To overcome this difficulty, we have devised a writing structure involving a two-line jingle, rather like that of an old-fashioned train track, which the children can fit their response into. In this example, the chant would be 'the bigger the force / the greater the stretch.' This focuses the children's ideas; they quickly get used to doing it and are pleased at being able to devise their own jingles. It provides a precise and concise format for expressing their ideas, but they still have to be able to identify the trend.

ABOUT THE *HANDLING SCIENCE DATA* SERIES
HOW THE BOOKS ARE ORGANISED

Each book in this series contains at least 25 activities, each comprising a page of teacher's notes and a photocopiable children's page. Occasionally, additional photocopiable resource pages are also provided. Each activity provides data related to one of the curricula for life processes and living things, materials, and physical processes, together with a set of questions related to interpreting the data.

The choice of science topics in this series has primarily been matched to the QCA's *Science Scheme of Work for Key Stage 2*, which many teachers in England are now using. However, the other UK curriculum documents have also been considered, and the teacher's notes give references for the National Curriculum in England, relevant units in the QCA's *Science Scheme of Work* and the Scottish National Guidelines for Science 5–14. It is intended that the activities can be used alongside any primary science scheme of work as reinforcement or revision. The level of work has also been matched to the National numeracy and literacy strategies, so that the work is set at an appropriate level, with suitable progression for the children in each year group.

FEATURES OF THE PHOTOCOPIABLES

The photocopiable worksheets in each book cater for a range of abilities in relation to graphical interpretation skills. On the worksheets, questions are generally arranged in increasing difficulty: some are deliberately challenging to extend the most able children. The majority of the questions are simply about interpreting the data, so the children need not have done the investigation described in order to be able to answer the questions.

Some of the questions identify the key scientific ideas that are relevant to that investigation. It is hoped that the children will have internalised these key concepts, if they have explored the topic practically already. Some questions are deliberately open-ended so they can be used as extension or research exercises, and provide ideal homework material. The questions cover a range of types and include:

- taking readings from graphs
- relating data to properties
- identifying and predicting trends
- investigative skills
- graph plotting and table design
- science understanding
- visualising an investigation.

The level of language varies between the different activities, and some children may need support with reading some of the worksheets. However, the topics do require technical vocabulary, so it is important that this is introduced and reinforced through any complementary lessons. One way to do this would be to let the children carry out the investigations themselves, then to use these sheets to provide matching practice or revision material.

The system of notation used for the quoting of units in this series is *factor/unit*, for example temperature/°C, or mass/g. This is the accepted format at all levels of science (and recommended by the ASE), although brackets – temperature (°C), or mass (g) – are acceptable at school ages. It is good practice for children to learn to put units at the top of each column in a table when recording data. This is the mathematical justification for using the '/': everything in the column below is divided by the unit, hence /*unit*, and only the numbers need to be written in the columns. Equally, when using spreadsheets, software will not recognise a cell that contains both text and numbers, so the children need to remember just to use numbers.

FEATURES OF THE TEACHERS' NOTES

We feel strongly that the most valuable way to help the children engage with science is by carrying out activities that provide outcomes (which could be data or observations) around which a class discussion can take place. Almost all of the data presented here has come from actual children's work. These are tried and tested activities, although the nature of practical investigations suggests they do not always work as successfully each time. All of the activities carry practical advice on how to carry out the activities that underpin the data. Some of these activities will be familiar to you, others not. Don't be afraid to try them out; the children will respond to them in a positive way and the data is much more meaningful if it is 'real'.

Even the most experienced and qualified science teachers learn new things all the time; you cannot hope to remember everything you did at school or university (even if you went to all the lectures!) Very few primary teachers have the luxury of a post-16 science education, yet they are expected to be in a position to be able to answer a wide range of children's questions. The teacher's notes provided with each activity give the answers to the questions on the worksheets (always useful!), together with the relevant background science associated with the activity. This is to assist you in dealing with questions that, in our experience, the enquiring minds of primary children might come up with, especially if your teaching is open-ended. These notes are not intended to state what you should teach the children about any topic, but to support your knowledge so you that you can internalise the concepts and then deal more effectively with the children's ideas.

ABOUT *HANDLING SCIENCE DATA: YEAR 4*

The activities in this book largely follow the topics covered in Year 4 of the QCA's *Science Scheme of Work,* and are also aimed at Level C of the Scottish *National Guidelines for Science* 5–14. The majority of the graphs are pictograms and bar graphs, and some line graphs are introduced. Creating pie charts is not considered appropriate for Year 4 children, due to the understanding of circle measurement and of fractions and percentages that is required. However, we have found that 8- and 9-year-olds can judge *relative* proportions from just looking at a simple pie chart, so pie charts using halves, quarters and so on are used.

USING COMPUTERS IN PRIMARY SCIENCE LESSONS

Confidence with the use of computers is increasing all the time, as is their availability. The majority of primary classrooms now contain a computer. Even so, most computer-based learning activities involve either using commercial software that provides children with interactive exercises or using the computer as a research tool. Many teachers are still not confident about using computers as an integral tool for learning science.

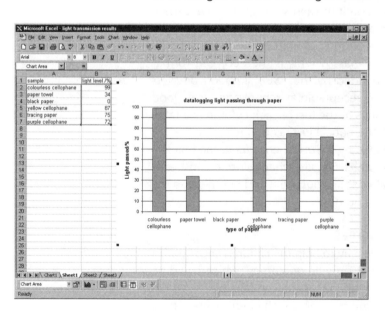

Nearly all of the activities in this series are derived from classroom investigations where, in addition to writing the results in an exercise book or science folder, we have computerised data as a spreadsheet with a graph-plotting facility. The spreadsheet and graph can be used as a method of displaying, and more importantly, analysing the data. Information handling and working with spreadsheets (and databases) is developed throughout the QCA's *ICT Scheme of Work* in Key Stage 2.

If the data is 'live' and on screen, children can predict the effect of changes in results to the appearance of the graph and check it instantaneously. If a result appears anomalous, the correct result can be predicted, inserted into the table and the effect observed immediately in the graph. This develops the skill of identifying trends in the data, but at the same time demonstrates the value of careful measurement, which at a younger age children do not always readily appreciate. When they repeat the result, they will more often than not take more care (or you can intervene and discuss possible sources of error). This can simultaneously develop practical skills.

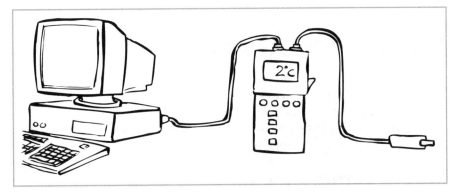

Each book in the series involves some examples of data collected by data-logging. This is a method of using electronic sensors to detect changes in light, temperature and sound, and then storing the data that can be processed using appropriate computer software. This is specifically a feature of the QCA's *ICT Scheme of Work* in Years 5 and 6 (Units 5F and 6C).

Our research findings, confirmed by our own experiences, suggest that children are much better at interpreting graphs when the data is 'live' – for example, being plotted by the computer as the investigation is carried out.

USEFUL PRACTICAL TECHNIQUES

Adjustable ramps are very useful pieces of equipment for a range of investigations, but commercial ones are normally too expensive for a school to have more than one. Here is a design for a ramp that is cheap and easily made. All you need is some corroflute (corrugated plastic sheeting), string and a spring toggle – then you just follow the instructions below.

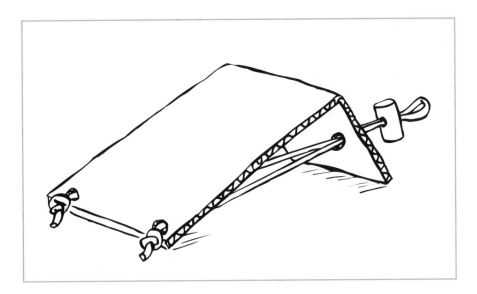

Take a length of corroflute and use a craft knife to cut through one surface (along a corrugation, not across), making a hinge. Use a hole punch to make the holes. Attach the string and toggle.

REFERENCES
1. RM Taylor and P Swatton, *Assessment Matters No.1: Graph Work In School Science* (APU, 1991)
2. A Goldsworthy, R Watson and V Wood Robinson, *Getting to Grips with Graphs, Investigations, Developing Understanding* (ASE, 2000)
3. *Standards at Key Stage 2 1996–2000* (QCA, 2001)

POND LIFE JIGSAW

National Curriculum Science KS2 PoS Sc2: 4b, c; 5a, b, d, e, f
QCA Science Unit 4B: Habitats
Scottish 5–14 Guidelines Variety and characteristic features – Level B;
Interaction of living things with their environment – Level B

HOW TO GATHER THE DATA

Pond-dipping is always a popular activity with children. It is essential that they are prepared beforehand so that they will take appropriate care of themselves and the pond life. When children go pond-dipping, they are often impatient and immediately scour the bottom of the pond, disturbing all the sludge. Persuade them to do things in a more productive order, as follows. **Step 1:** look above the pond and on its surface for creatures such as dragonflies and pond skaters. **Step 2:** look for creatures that are moving around underneath the surface (such as water boatmen, fish and newts), and catch these with as little disturbance of the water as possible. **Step 3:** dredge the bottom of the pond for creatures that feed on dead matter, such as snails and worms.

Some other points to remember are: *Do not go alone or trespass on private areas. Do not throw litter. Use a proper jetty or platform if there is one. Return your catches to the pond. Never drink pond water and always wash your hands afterwards. Use a measuring stick to check the depth of the pond before you step or reach into it.*

THE SCIENCE BEHIND THE DATA

A habitat is a place where a plant or an animal lives. A food chain is a diagram that shows feeding relationships in a habitat. A food chain always starts with a producer (green plants or algae) that uses the Sun's energy to produce its own food (biomass) by photosynthesis. Thus all food chains have the Sun as their ultimate energy source. All the organisms that come after the producer in a food chain are animals, known as consumers. Primary consumers only eat producers; animals higher up the food chain are secondary consumers that eat other animals (and possibly plants as well). Secondary consumers that kill other animals for food are known as predators, and the animals they kill are known as prey. Some food chains start with dead matter, which is the product of other food chains.

A food chain is always drawn with arrows to show the direction in which food (and thus energy) flows:

producer $\Longrightarrow$ primary consumer $\Longrightarrow$ secondary consumer

There are usually several food chains within a single habitat. A combination of linked food chains is called a food web. A habitat together with the organisms that live there is called an ecosystem. A pond is an example of a self-contained and balanced ecosystem. Use Question 10 to emphasise that the children should replace the things they catch, so that they do not disrupt the ecosystem.

Answers

1. Completed as shown on page 62.
2. An organism that makes its own food from the Sun's energy. Any example from the inner ring of the jigsaw except dead matter.
3. An animal that eats plants or other animals. Any example from the two outer rings of the diagram.
4. An animal that kills and eats other animals. Lesser water boatman or any example from the outer ring of the diagram.
5. Several answers are possible, each starting with a producer (or with dead matter).
6. Several answers are possible, each starting with a producer and including a sideways jigsaw connection (involving the small pond snail or the tadpole).
7. Algae. Newt or stickleback.
8. Water louse.
9. Examples might include:

	Animal 1	**Animal 2**	**Animal 3**
Name of creature	Stickleback	Snail	Water flea
How does it move?	Swims	Slides	Swims/paddles
How fast is it?	Fast	Slow	Quite fast
How many legs does it have?	None	None (foot)	Many
What does it eat?	Lesser water beetle	Algae, plants	Micro. plants
How does it protect itself?	Spines (barbs)	Hard shell	With difficulty

10. Several things could happen that would upset the balance of the ecosystem: all the sticklebacks die through lack of food; the newts eat more snails and tadpoles; the great diving beetles eat more snails, water lice and water fleas; there are more snails; and so on. Effects on the levels of producers and dead matter are also possible.

Pond life jigsaw

The jigsaw on page 62 shows the feeding relationships between some plants and animals found in a pond.

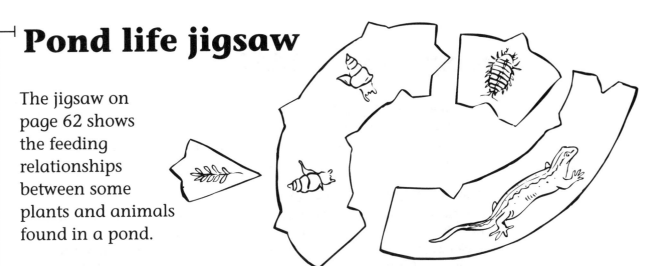

Questions

1. Cut out the jigsaw pieces from page 62 and fit them together to make a complete pond life jigsaw. Now use your jigsaw to answer the following questions.

2. What is a producer? Give an example from your jigsaw.

3. What is a consumer? Give an example from your jigsaw.

4. What is a predator? Give an example from your jigsaw.

5. Construct a pond food chain containing three species. Make sure you draw the arrows pointing the correct way.

6. Construct a pond food chain containing four species. Make sure you draw the arrows pointing the correct way.

7. Find the lesser water boatman on the jigsaw. Name one thing that the lesser water boatman eats, and name one thing that eats the lesser water boatman.

8. Which animal eats dead matter?

9. Use your jigsaw to help you complete this table for three animals.

	Animal 1	**Animal 2**	**Animal 3**
Name of animal			
How does it move?			
How fast is it?			
How many legs does it have?			
What does it eat?			
How does it protect itself?			

10. Look at the jigsaw. Can you predict what might happen if all the lesser water boatmen were taken out of the pond?

HANDLING SCIENCE DATA YEAR 4

MINIBEAST SAFARI

National Curriculum Science KS2 PoS Sc2: 5a, b, c
QCA Science Unit 4B: Habitats
Scottish 5–14 Guidelines Variety and characteristic features – Level B;
Interaction of living things with their environment – Levels A, D

HOW TO GATHER THE DATA

For this activity, you need a wild area in the school grounds; but this does not have to be a school field. Sometimes an enclosed area is better, because it will not be disturbed. All you need is a pile of old stones and a pile of logs that can rot away (preferably on a soil base). Also, a piece of stiff black plastic is good for encouraging worms to come to the surface, since it stops moisture evaporating from the soil so the worms will stay close to the surface.

Literature is available – for example, Nottingham Wildlife Trust have an excellent website (www.wildkids.org.uk) that describes how to create minibeast environments. The children need to be careful how they lift up logs or rocks, they should always replace them in the same position. It may help the children to spot some smaller crawling animals if they move the log or rock and then just stare at the space they have created: minibeasts will appear before their eyes!

THE SCIENCE BEHIND THE DATA

Animals such as slugs, snails and worms thrive in dark, damp places, and worms will come to the surface if the ground is very wet – hence the greater number of 'slimy' minibeasts found in April. Spiders and mosquitoes will appear when the weather is warmer and drier. Also, minibeasts will be more active and present in greater numbers in warm summer weather than in the spring, because there is more food available for them: more plant material for primary consumers, and thus more prey available for insect-eating predators (such as spiders) and parasites (such as mosquitoes).

Answers

1. Worms.
2. Mosquitoes.
3. The weather was very wet, so slimy creatures such as worms and slugs were more likely to be found.
4. 5
5. a) under logs, where it is damp **b)** in hedges or in spaces between rocks, to spin webs **c)** in hidden corners underneath logs or rocks, where it is damp.
6. Mosquitoes.
7. Worms.
8. The weather was warmer and drier than in April, so the worms and slugs stay hidden and the numbers found are lower. Mosquitoes appear when the weather is warmer and they can feed on other insects and mammals (but they gather in more humid places such as hedges).
9. 7
10. The warmer weather means that all the creatures are active and feeding. There is more plant food available for primary consumers such as flying insects, which also means that more prey are available for predators such as spiders – so the overall number of minibeasts increases.

Minibeast safari

Class 4 went on a minibeast safari in the school grounds in April. It was quite cold, and it had been raining heavily. They looked under some logs and stones, and in the hedge. They were very careful about how they handled all the animals they found. They counted how many animals of each type they found, using a tally chart.

When they went inside, they made a graph of everything the class had seen.

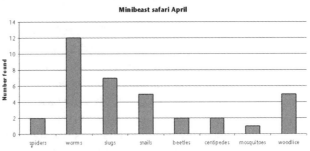

Questions

1. What animal were there most of?

2. What animal were there least of?

3. How do you think the weather has affected which animals the children found?

4. How many snails were there?

5. Where do you think the children would find **a)** the woodlice, **b)** the spiders, **c)** the snails? Explain your answer each time.

The children went on safari again in June, when the weather had been hot and dry. They found a different number of each type of minibeast from before.

Their graph is shown on the right.

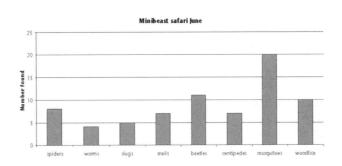

6. What animal were there most of?

7. What animal were there least of?

8. How do you think the weather has affected which animals the children found?

9. How many millipedes were there?

10. When the children did this activity in April, they found 36 minibeasts. In June, they found 72 minibeasts. Why do you think there was such a difference?

LITTLE GAME HUNT

National Curriculum Science KS2 PoS Sc2: 5a, b, c
QCA Science Unit 4B: Habitats
Scottish 5–14 Guidelines Variety and characteristic features – Level B;
Interaction of living things with their environment – Level D

HOW TO GATHER THE DATA

For this activity, you need a wild area in the school grounds; but this does not have to be a school field. Sometimes an enclosed area is better, because it will not be disturbed. All you need is a pile of old stones and a pile of logs that can rot away (preferably on a soil base). Also, a piece of stiff black plastic is good for encouraging worms to come to the surface, since it stops moisture evaporating from the soil so the worms will stay close to the surface.

Literature is available that describes how to create minibeast environments – for example, Nottingham Wildlife Trust have an excellent website (www. wildkids.org.uk). The children need to be careful how they lift up logs or rocks, they should always replace them in the same position. It may help the children to spot some smaller crawling animals if they move the log or rock and then just stare at the space they have created: minibeasts will appear before their eyes!

THE SCIENCE BEHIND THE DATA

In this activity, the categorisation of minibeasts as 'sliders', 'crawlers' and 'flyers' helps the children to understand the scientific explanations of the data. Animals such as slugs, snails and worms thrive in dark, damp places, where it is easier for them to move and breathe. Worms will come to the surface if the ground is very wet, hence the greater number of 'sliders' found in April. 'Crawlers' (such as woodlice) and 'flyers' (such as mosquitoes) will appear when the weather is warmer and drier and it is easier for them to find food. Also, minibeasts will be more active and present in greater numbers in warm summer weather than in the spring, because there is more food available for them: more plant material for primary consumers, and thus more prey available for insect-eating predators such as spiders.

Answers

1. Sliders.
2. Flyers.
3. Slugs, snails or worms.
4. The animals that 'slide' (for example, worms and slugs) are slimy and so need lots of moisture. They are more likely to be found when the weather is very wet.
5. Underneath logs and rocks, where it is wet and cool.
6. Slimy creatures need damp conditions so they can move more easily, and the soil is wetter underneath things (since there is less evaporation).
7. Crawlers.
8. Sliders.
9. When the weather is drier and hotter, slimy animals such as worms go further underground to find moister conditions. Flying creatures (insects) are more active in warmer weather because there is more plant food for them.
10. The warmer weather in June means that all the creatures are fully active and feeding. The primary consumers feed on plants (either leaves or nectar from flowers), and there is more food for insect-eating predators such as spiders. So the overall number of minibeasts is higher than in April.

Little game hunt

Class 4 went on a 'little game hunt' in the school grounds in April. It was quite cold, and it had been raining heavily. They looked under some logs and stones, and in the hedge. They were very careful about how they handled all the creatures they found. They counted how many minibeasts of each type they found, using a tally chart.

Back in the classroom, they made a pie chart to show what they had seen.

sliders
crawlers
flyers

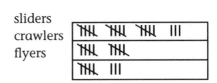

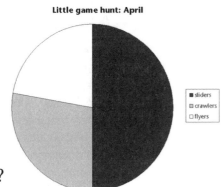

Little game hunt: April

■ sliders
▨ crawlers
▢ flyers

Questions

1. What group of animal were there most of?

2. What group were there least of?

3. Name an animal they might have found that would be included in the group 'sliders'.

4. How do you think the weather has affected what types of animal the children found?

5. Where do you think the children found the 'sliders'?

6. Explain your answer to Question 5.

The children repeated their 'little game hunt' in June, when the weather had been hot and dry. They found a different number of each group of minibeasts from before. Their results are shown in the pie chart below.

7. What group of animals were there most of?

8. What group were there least of?

9. How do you think the weather has affected what species the children found?

10. When the children did the activity in April, they found 36 minibeasts. In June, they found 72 minibeasts. Why do you think there is such a difference?

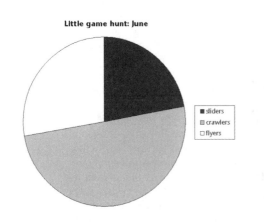

Little game hunt: June

■ sliders
▨ crawlers
▢ flyers

WHAT PLANTS GROW IN OUR LAWN?

> **National Curriculum Science** KS2 PoS Sc2: 5a,b
> **QCA Science** Unit 4B: Habitats
> **Scottish 5–14 Guidelines** Interaction of living things with their environment – Levels A, C, D

HOW TO GATHER THE DATA

You will need to introduce the children to the idea of taking random samples from different parts of a lawn. Explain why it is best to take several samples from each part of the lawn: in the middle (as this group did) and at the edges. Discuss the difference between the group's initial sketch map (which does not represent a real area) and their bar graph (which represents the data for ten real areas). A Year 4 class can be organised into three groups of about ten children to survey different areas of the lawn (for example, the middle, the edge and an area near some trees). Pairs within the group could carry out two quadrat surveys each. Collapsible half-metre quadrats can be obtained from most primary science suppliers.

Answers

1. A lawn is sown with grass seeds, which have 'creeping' growth (one grass plant can spread enough to cover an acre, which is almost the size of a football pitch).
2. Artificial.
3. Clover.
4. Buttercup or plantain.
5. 2
6. 6
7. Using quadrats to provide a sample of areas enabled the group to survey the plants in the lawn in a more complete and systematic way. The children looked at ten quadrats which were placed at random. One quadrat might have given results that were not typical – for example, a particular small area might have contained a cluster of dandelion plants.
8. Their leaves are close to the ground, they have strong roots and they are tough enough to survive when people tread on them.
9. The children may suggest a number of factors, including: amount of sunlight, amount of rain, type of soil, time of year, people walking on the grass and people mowing the grass. The last two factors are probably the most significant.
10. There may be fewer plants near the path, because people often walk on the edge of the lawn. The grass is likely to be thinner, but the most strongly rooted plants (such as dandelions and plantain) would probably be found.

THE SCIENCE BEHIND THE DATA

Possible factors that may affect the species of plant found in this habitat include light intensity, wind, temperature, moisture, soil pH, competition between plant species, seasonal changes, mowing and people walking on the grass. The children may only suggest some of these at this stage in their learning, but it is important for them to recognise that the last two are probably the most significant. Discuss with them the effects that mowing and trampling have on the species that have been found in the grass, and how these plants are able to survive in spite of these problems. Using pictures of the plants from books or CD-ROMs will aid the discussion.

The plants found in a lawn are well adapted to this artificially produced habitat because they are able to reproduce without growing tall. The children could observe this on a lawn or regularly cut school field. Each of the plants also has distinct features that assist its survival in this habitat:

- Dandelion – superb seed dispersal and production, leaves close to the ground, tap root able to produce new leaves even when the plant is damaged.
- Clover – the plant creeps and puts down roots at the same time.
- Daisy – the rosettes grow very close to the ground.
- Plantain – leaves close to the ground, tough stem and leaves resist being trampled on, has a strong tap root.

What plants grow in our lawn?

Ranjit, Amy, Jayne and Adam investigated what types of plant were growing in the lawn in front of their school. Based on their first general impression, they drew a sketch map (not to scale) to show how various plants might be typically distributed in a square metre of lawn.

The children then decided to investigate in a more systematic way. They carried out a survey of ten 0.5m quadrats in the middle of the lawn, and recorded the total number of plant species in the ten quadrats placed at random in the garden. They plotted their results as a bar graph.

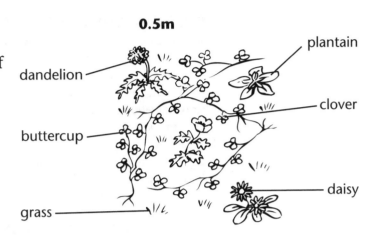

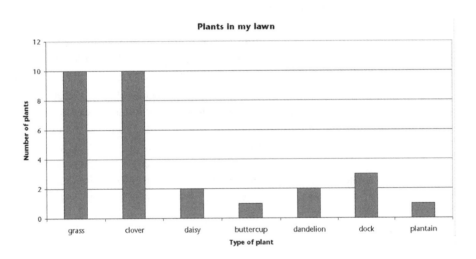

Questions

1. Why were grass plants found in all the quadrats?

2. What type of habitat is a lawn: natural or artificial?

3. What was the most common plant, other than grass, found in the lawn?

4. What was the least common plant found in the lawn?

5. How many daisy plants were found?

6. How many types of plant, other than grass, were found in the lawn?

7. Why did the group survey ten quadrats in the lawn rather than one?

8. What were the common features of the plants found in the lawn?

9. What factors might affect the types of plant growing in the lawn?

10. If another group of children carried out ten quadrat measurements near a path at the edge of the lawn, what differences might they have found?

HANDLING SCIENCE DATA YEAR 4

KEYS

National Curriculum Science KS2 PoS Sc2: 4a, b
QCA Science Unit 4B: Habitats
Scottish 5–14 Guidelines Variety and characteristic features – Level C

HOW TO GATHER THE DATA

This key leads children to identify some animals that they may have come across and that have fairly obvious distinguishing features. Identification keys are available in various published resources, or you can design your own. They can be matched to the ability of the children, and can be used to develop their observation skills. You can use the animals or plants that you find locally to design a key that the children will find useful in their own minibeast hunts. The Internet is a good source of reference material , but you must not cut and paste images from it without permission. Keys can be used not only for animals and plants, but for materials, which can be classified according to their various properties.

THE SCIENCE BEHIND THE DATA

Using keys enables both scientists and non-scientists to identify species of animal or plant from their appearance. A key uses observable distinguishing features to lead the observer to the name of the species. There are two types of key – the activity opposite is an example of a branching key. It presents a series of Yes/No questions that narrow down the options at each stage, until the subject is identified. Another type of key has a series of numbered statements, each of which directs you to a choice of possible further statements.

Although the two types of key lead the user to accumulate information in a similar way, evidence shows that children find numerical keys more difficult to use. However, a numerical key can be used to present more elaborate descriptions than a branched key, and this often aids identification. The branched key in this activity could be written in a numerical format:

1. it has four legs	go to 2
it does not have four legs	go to 4
2. it has a tail	go to 3
it does not have a tail	frog
3. it has big scary teeth	lion
it does not have big scary teeth	dormouse
4. it has wings	go to 5
it does not have wings	plaice
5. it has feathers	falcon
it does not have feathers	dragonfly

Answers

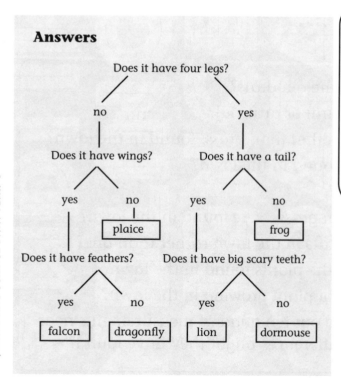

Keys

Lucy has six unusual pets. She is writing a key to help her friends identify them.

frog

plaice

falcon

dragonfly

lion

dormouse

Questions

Can you finish the key by writing the names of the animals in the six empty boxes?

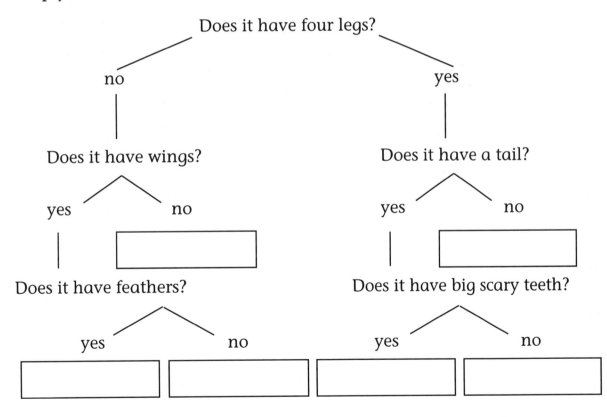

Does it have four legs?

no   yes

Does it have wings?   Does it have a tail?

yes   no   yes   no

Does it have feathers?   Does it have big scary teeth?

yes   no   yes   no

GROWING UP

National Curriculum Science KS2 PoS Sc2: 1a; 2f
QCA Science Unit 4A: Moving and growing
Scottish 5–14 Guidelines The processes of life – Level B

HOW TO GATHER THE DATA

This information can be gathered from a wide variety of sources, such as www. riverdeep.net (both the maths and science sections contain useful information and data). The children could gather their own data by measuring other children in the school and members of their families, then use other sources to fill in the gaps. A life-size display can be made by drawing round volunteers of different ages and heights on wallpaper, painting pictures inside the outlines and pinning them up.

THE SCIENCE BEHIND THE DATA

The growth and development rates of children are faster than in later life. At birth, the average weight of a baby is 3.4kg and the average height is 50cm. A baby's torso is 70% of body length, but an adult's torso is only 52% of body length. Girls reach 50% of adult height before 2 years of age, boys at around 2 years. From birth to 20 years, the body length increases 3–4 times and the mass increases 20 times.

Boys begin the growth spurt associated with puberty at around 11.5 years; it lasts until around 14 years. For girls, the growth spurt starts at around 9 years, reaches its maximum rate around 12 years and is completed at around 16 years. Within the adolescent 'growth spurt', teens and pre-teens experience 'mini-spurts' of intense growth. They may experience 'growing pains' as their skeletons develop. During a one-year period of intense growth, boys can gain about 10.2cm and girls about 8.9cm in height. A team of scientists recently discovered that the brain also grows during puberty. In children aged 15 and younger, the most brain growth is in the part of the brain linked to the ability to learn languages and think abstractly.

The average heights of adults decline steadily with age after 20 years. Around 40 years of age, most people begin to shrink in stature. Women shrink more than men and shrinkage accelerates with age. This shrinkage occurs in the discs of the spine, often causing rounding of the back. Some reduction in height may result from shrinkage of lower limbs around the joints. (Height also varies with time of day – because the discs of the spinal column are compressed by body weight throughout the day, we tend to be slightly shorter in the evening.)

Answers

1 and 2. Completed diagram with 4 pictures in order:
3. 50cm, 90cm, 165cm, 185cm
4. 50cm
5. 13–15
6. A bar at 185cm.
7. 185cm
8. Beyond the age of 21 or so, adults do not grow any taller.

Growing up

We cannot be born at full size, so we grow bigger as we get older. Page 63 shows pictures of a baby, a toddler, a teenager and an adult, drawn to scale.

Questions

1. Cut out the pictures of the baby, toddler, teenager and adult from page 63.

2. Stick them on the graph on page 63 in the correct order.

3. Use the axes on the graph to measure how tall each one is. Write the height next to each picture.

The graph below shows the average height at different ages of a range of people. Use it to answer the next set of questions.

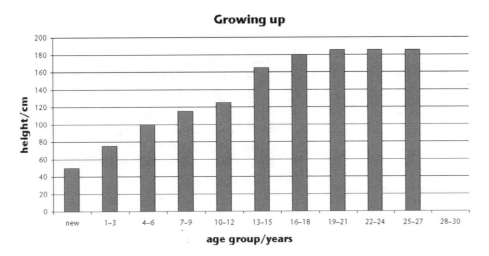

4. How tall is an average newborn baby?

5. Which age group shows the biggest difference in height from the previous age group?

6. Draw a bar showing what you think will be the average height for the age group 28–30.

7. What do you think will be the average height at age 40?

8. Explain your answer to Question 7.

HANDLING SCIENCE DATA YEAR 4

HOW DO WE GROW?

National Curriculum Science KS2 PoS Sc2 1a; 2f
QCA Science Unit 4A: Moving and growing
Scottish 5–14 Guidelines The processes of life – Level B

HOW TO GATHER THE DATA

Children do not need to compare median, mode and mean averages until Year 6. However, the realistic context of this work makes it appropriate for providing a simple introduction to the concept of a median average. Explain that Class 4 chose the child with the middle height because he or she would be an 'average' child – it saved measuring all the heights to work out an average, and it avoided the problem of the average value being affected by an unusually tall or short child. These are actual data that were collected by real children; if your class repeats the data-gathering process, you will probably obtain slightly different results. These could be used to stimulate discussion of the idea that variation in properties such as height is natural and is to be expected: between groups as between individuals, there is no 'normal' value for height.

Answers
1. Thighbone (femur).
2. Yes.
3. The bars are getting longer each year.
4. Reception to Year 1.
5. Year 2 to Year 3.
6.

Year	Height/cm	Hip to knee/cm
Reception	95	19
Year 1	118	30
Year 2	128	33
Year 3	129	34
Year 4	134	38
Year 5	146	41
Year 6	156	45
Year 7		

7. Height greater than for Year 6, but not above 175cm or so. Hip to knee length greater than for Year 6, but not above 50cm or so.
8. The child's explanation might state that during childhood we grow taller by about 5–10cm each year, except during the phases of exceptionally rapid growth ('growth spurts') at the toddler stage and then at the start of puberty. The child may also observe that the increase in the length of the thighbone each year accounts for nearly half of the overall increase in height.
9. A bar indicating the child's height should be drawn to the left of the 'height' bar for Year 4.
10. The child should respond according to whether he or she is taller or shorter than the 'middle' child in Year 4 on the graph.

THE SCIENCE BEHIND THE DATA

Children grow taller as they become older, but the increase in height is not a steady process. The graph on page 23 shows height increasing initially (the rapid growth of the 'toddler' stage), then levelling off over Years 2 and 3 (the 'lull' before the 'growth spurt'), then increasing again (the start of the 'growth spurt').

The pubertal 'growth spurt' usually begins around the age of 9 in girls and 11 in boys, but there are many exceptions. Diet, activity and genetic factors all affect growth rates.

Body proportions change with growth. The main factor in increasing height is the length of the leg. In the graph shown on page 23, the increase in thigh length is nearly half the overall increase in height. Most adults, when sitting down, appear to be of similar height.

How do we grow?

Class 4 measured one child from each year class in the school. They lined up the class and chose the child with the middle height. For each child they had chosen, they measured their height and the distance from hip to knee.

Here is a graph of their results.

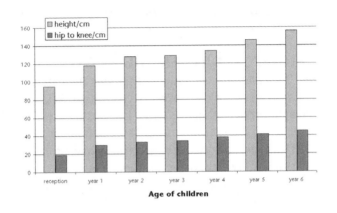

Questions

1. What is the common name for the bone from the hip to the knee?

2. Does the length of this bone in a child increase each year?

3. How can you tell from the graph?

4. When is the largest increase in child height between one year and the next?

5. When is the smallest increase in child height between one year and the next?

6. Complete this table to show the data for the graph above.

	Height/cm	Hip to knee/cm
Reception		
Year 1		
Year 2		
Year 3		
Year 4		
Year 5		
Year 6		
Year 7		

7. For Year 7, predict what the height and hip-to-knee length will be. Write your answers in the table.

8. Explain your predictions in Question 7.

9. Measure your own height. On the graph, draw a bar for your height next to the bar showing the middle height for your year group.

10. Are you taller or shorter than the middle person in your year group on the graph?

USING MUSCLES

National Curriculum Science KS2 PoS: Sc2 2d
QCA Science Unit 4A: Moving and growing
Scottish 5–14 Guidelines Variety and characteristic features – Level A; Forces and their effects – Level B

HOW TO GATHER THE DATA

The children can easily gather this data, and Plasticine is usually available from an infant class. Weighing is the quickest way of ensuring that a constant amount of Plasticine is used. The Plasticine will need to be softened up before starting the measurement. The children can use a tape measure for both the Plasticine and the muscles. The actual process of the investigation is quite straightforward, so this is a good activity for discussing the method, the choice of equipment and the factors that might influence the results. Depending on the children's ability, you could also discuss the reliability of the data.

The children can start by predicting who in the class will be able to squash the Plasticine the most, then give reasons (such as size of biceps muscle, size of hand or length of arm). To make this a fair test, they need to keep these factors the same: the amount of Plasticine, the procedure for squashing it (for example, a single act of squeezing), the same initial condition (softness) of the Plasticine. Might the colour of the Plasticine affect the outcome?

Answers

1. 9cm
2. 3.5cm
3. 30cm
4. Yes.
5. The first bar on the graph, representing the smallest biceps, is also the shortest and so represents the least amount of squash.
6. Approximately 26cm.
7. Look for appropriate planning in the four areas described.
a) Change the muscle size (i.e. use this to order and group the data).
b) Use the same amount of Plasticine; use Plasticine of the same softness and (possibly) colour; use the same procedure for squashing.
c) Measure the circumference of the Plasticine ball (before squashing) and disc (after squashing).
d) A table such as:

THE SCIENCE BEHIND THE DATA

The squashing action uses the biceps and triceps muscles in the upper arm, and also the forearm muscles (flexor and extensor carpi radialis and flexor and extensor carpi ulnaris). The biceps (together with the triceps) is probably the muscle that the children will choose to measure. The data used in the graph on page 25 is taken from real Year 4 children, and shows that the biggest arm is not necessarily the strongest: the children with the biggest upper arms had more fat on their upper arms and not more muscle. This idea may need to be handled carefully and sensitively with the children in your class.

Muscle size/cm	Initial circumference/cm	Squash/cm	Final circumference/cm

Using muscles

Class 4 were having a competition to see who could squash a ball of Plasticine the most. Faiyaz thought the person with the biggest arm muscle (biceps) would squash the Plasticine the most, so the class tried this out.

They took turns to roll 40g of Plasticine into a ball and squash it between their hands. They measured the circumference of the ball with a tape measure before squashing it, and measured the circumference of the flattened disc produced by squashing: the increase in the circumference indicated the amount of squash. Then they measured the circumference of their biceps muscles.

Finally, Class 4 drew a bar graph of the average results, showing the biceps sizes and how far the children could squash the Plasticine.

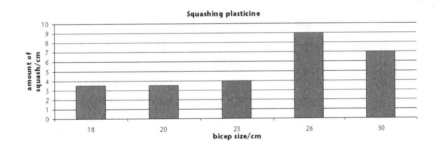

Questions

1. What was the biggest amount of squash?

2. What was the smallest amount of squash?

3. What was the biggest biceps size?

4. Do the smallest biceps give the smallest squash?

5. Explain how you decided that from the graph.

6. What seems to be the best biceps size to give the biggest squash?

7. Write a full plan to help another class repeat this investigation. In your plan, you should include these things:

a) what to change each time

b) what to measure each time

c) what to keep the same each time

d) a blank results table showing the headings and units.

HANDLING SCIENCE DATA YEAR 4

ICE POPS

National Curriculum Science KS2 PoS Sc3: 1b; 2c
QCA Science Unit 4C: Keeping warm
Scottish 5–14 Guidelines Materials from Earth – Levels A, B

HOW TO GATHER THE DATA

This investigation was suggested and devised by a Year 4 pupil, and shows the benefit of giving children ownership of their work. Ice pops are particularly suitable for this type of investigation, because the plastic wrapper keeps the melted liquid inside until the bottom is cut open. Also, because the liquids tend to be brightly coloured, they are easy to see and compare. If you do not have measuring cylinders that can measure very small amounts of liquid, you can use medicine pots (available from a local pharmacy) to measure the liquid: these are calibrated, plastic and quite easy for children to handle. Resource page 64 can be used to provide a set of blank graph axes.

Answers

1.

Wrapping	Amount of liquid/cm³
newspaper	15
cling film	25
cooking foil	30
polystyrene	7
bubble wrap	9
tea towel	20

2.

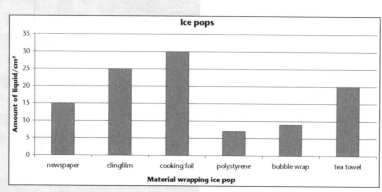

3. Cooking foil.
4. Polystyrene.
5. The ice pop wrapped in this material produced the least amount of liquid.
6. Thermal insulator.
7. Thermal conductor.
8. The ice pops should have been at the same initial temperature. They should have been kept in the same place (at the same temperature) during the investigation.
9. Approximately 15cm³.
10. The newspaper gave this amount, and kitchen roll is made from paper.

THE SCIENCE BEHIND THE DATA

Keeping things either hot or cold involves using a thermal insulator to stop heat transfer. Heat is always transferred from a hotter place to a colder one, but 'cold' is not something in itself: it is simply a relative lack of heat. The 'cold' of the ice pop does not escape in this activity: the room is warmer, so heat from the surroundings passes into the ice pop.

When a material is heated, the particles gain energy and move faster. Heat can be transferred from one place to another in three different ways:

1. Conduction – particles vibrate faster and pass on their vibrations to the particles next to them. Metals are good conductors of heat, because their electrons can move easily to transfer energy. Non-metals and liquids are poor conductors. Gases are very poor conductors, and conduction cannot take place through a vacuum.

2. Convection – in liquids and gases, the particles are free to move about. If they are heated, they move faster and spread out more, carrying energy with them. Because the density is less, the warmer liquid or gas will rise.

3. Radiation – all objects give out infra-red (heat) radiation. Very hot objects (such as a light bulb filament) give out visible light as well. This way of transferring heat energy does not require other particles. For example, the Sun's heat energy travels across the near-vacuum of space. Shiny, bright surfaces are the poorest radiators of heat; dark, dull surfaces are the best radiators. The same principle applies to absorbing radiation: dark clothes absorb heat better than light clothes.

Ice pops

Jordan, Lewis, Paul and Marco were investigating which material is the best to stop their ice pops melting. In their discussion, Paul suggested that they could cover the unmelted ice pops with the materials, leave them, then measure how much liquid there was inside.

They wrapped up each ice pop with five layers of a material, left them all for 30 minutes, then removed the material and cut a hole in the bottom of each ice pop to let the liquid run out into a measuring cylinder.

Here are their results.

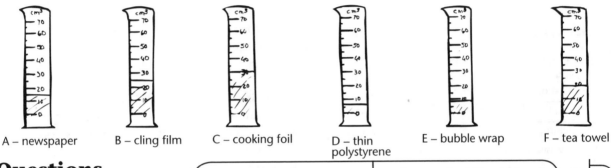

A – newspaper   B – cling film   C – cooking foil   D – thin polystyrene   E – bubble wrap   F – tea towel

Questions

1. Fill in the children's results in this table.

Wrapping	Amount of liquid/cm³

2. Draw a bar graph to show the children's results. You could use a set of blank graph axes for this. Remember to label the axes correctly.

3. Which wrapping material produced the most liquid?

4. Which wrapping material is the best for keeping an ice pop frozen?

5. How can you tell this from the graph?

6. What name do we give to a material that stops heat passing through it?

7. What name do we give to a material that lets heat pass through it?

8. Write down two other things that the children should have done to make sure their investigation is a fair test.

9. How much liquid do you think would be formed if the children wrapped the ice pop in kitchen roll?

10. Explain your answer to Question 9.

KEEPING WARM

National Curriculum Science KS2 PoS Sc3: 1b; 2c
QCA Science Unit 4C: Keeping warm
Scottish 5–14 Guidelines Materials from Earth – Level B; Properties and uses of energy – Level D

HOW TO GATHER THE DATA

This investigation is relatively easy to set up and carry out. You will need a good supply of plastic water bottles and a range of insulating materials. Organise the children into groups. Each group can choose which material to investigate, with one group carrying out the control investigation. Use warm water (about 50°C) rather than hot water, for safety reasons. It is probably best to fill the bottles yourself after the children have wrapped them up. If you fill them first, the children may spill some water and the remaining water will cool more quickly. Each group should measure and record the temperature of the water at the beginning and after 45 minutes have elapsed, then calculate the temperature change.

THE SCIENCE BEHIND THE DATA

Children know which materials keep them warm, but this investigation allows them to explore the reasons why. Many of them will predict that cotton wool is the best material for keeping the water bottle warm, because it is thick and has air trapped inside it. Air is a poor conductor of heat, so the bottle's heat will not be lost by conduction. It is worth drawing out the children's ideas, and sometimes their experience is wider than a teacher's – some children recently drew my attention to the fact that bubble wrap is used to keep premature babies warm. Brighter children may begin to understand the simple explanation that in air, the particles are far apart and heat energy is not readily passed from one particle to another, so materials with air trapped inside them are good thermal insulators. In contrast, metals are poor thermal insulators as the particles are close together and the electrons can move between particles, so energy passes easily from one particle to the next.

Answers

1. Cotton wool.
2. Cotton wool is a thick soft material with a lot of air trapped inside it. Air is a good insulator, so the heat is kept inside the bottle.
3. Recording the change in temperature makes it easier to compare the bottles. The change in temperature shows how much heat has been lost from the water into the surrounding air.
4. 15°C
5. 35°C. Make sure the children are clear that the **drop** in temperature has been plotted, and that they can calculate the temperature of the water after 45 minutes by subtracting the value plotted on the graph from 50°C.
6. 45°C
7. The unwrapped bottle showed how much heat was lost from the bottle without any wrapping being applied. This was necessary to judge how effective the materials were in insulating the bottle.
8. Both the bubble wrap and the kapok have air trapped in them. The air insulates the bottle and stops the heat being lost so quickly.
9. The type of bottle (size, shape, material), the volume of water, the initial temperature of the water, using one layer of the wrapping material, the time between temperature measurements.
10. It was not possible to keep the thickness of the materials the same. A layer of cotton wool is probably thicker than a layer of the other materials used.
11. Yes, this could have been the reason why cotton wool was the best insulator.
12. Various answers are possible. In winter we tend to wear thicker clothes – often made of wool, which traps air. Often winter coats are made of two materials: an outside rainproof layer and an inner insulating (fleecy) layer.
13. The children may suggest wool, cotton, sheepskin and so on. They could also investigate whether several thin layers of material are better for keeping things warm than one thick layer.

Keeping warm

A class of children wanted to find out what was the best material for keeping things warm. They investigated this by wrapping plastic bottles in different materials. The bottles were all the same size and shape, and each was fitted with a cap. One group did not wrap up their plastic bottle: it served as a 'control'. The other groups wrapped up their bottles in one layer of material, across the sides and round the bottom. All the groups carefully filled their bottles to the same height with warm water at the same temperature (50°C) and replaced the caps. They left the bottles for 45 minutes and measured the temperature again.

The children calculated the drop in temperature for each bottle, and recorded their results in a bar graph.

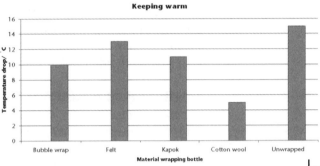

Questions

1. Which was the best material for keeping the water warm?

2. Why do you think this is?

3. The children showed the temperature drop on the graph rather than the final temperature. Why?

4. What was the temperature drop for the unwrapped bottle?

5. What was the temperature of the water in the unwrapped bottle after 45 minutes?

6. What was the temperature of the water in the bottle wrapped in cotton wool after 45 minutes?

7. Why did the children need to use an unwrapped bottle in their investigation?

8. The bubble wrap and the kapok were quite good for keeping things warm. Can you explain why?

9. List the factors that the children kept the same.

10. Which property of the materials do you think it was not possible to keep the same?

11. Do you think this may have affected the results?

12. Think about the clothes that you wear in the winter to keep warm. Are they similar to the materials that the children tested?

13. If you did this investigation, would you test the same materials as these children, or would you include others from your answer to Question 12? List four materials you would choose.

HANDLING SCIENCE DATA YEAR 4

HOW HOT IS IT?

National Curriculum Science KS2 PoS Sc3: 2c
QCA Science Unit 4C: Keeping warm
Scottish 5–14 Guidelines Properties and uses of energy – Levels B, D

HOW TO GATHER THE DATA

Many children have difficulty in using and reading the temperature on a thermometer. Dataloggers are usually much easier to use, and they give a digital readout on a screen. This investigation can be carried out using a datalogger such as Ecolog, where the external temperature probe is connected to the computer and the readings are recorded in SNAPSHOT mode. If a datalogger powered by a battery (LogIT, Explorer, Ecolog) is used, the children can record their measurements at different points in the classroom and then download them into the computer.

THE SCIENCE BEHIND THE DATA

It is important that children are given opportunities to measure temperature using thermometers and dataloggers. This practical experience will help them to understand that temperature is a measure of how hot or cold something is, not how much heat it contains. Think of relaxing in the bath with a freshly made cup of tea: the cup of tea is much hotter than the bath water (it has a higher temperature), but the bath water contains more heat than the tea because there is much more water in the bath. This is a difficult concept for children. You need to encourage them to describe things in a correct way, but you don't want to get so technical that it confuses them. The teacher is the only person who can judge the appropriate balance between accuracy and accessibility for a given class.

This activity will help children to link the temperature of the classroom to different seasons and different times of day. Changes in local temperature follow two cycles:

1. Daily change – the Sun radiates heat across space, and the Earth absorbs some of this. The part of the Earth that is in daylight is receiving more radiated heat than it emits, so its temperature rises. At night, that part of the Earth is not receiving direct radiation, so it radiates more heat into space than it receives and cools down. The Earth's atmosphere traps some of the heat radiated by the Earth and keeps the planet fairly warm. Without this 'greenhouse effect', we could not survive.

2. Seasonal change – in summer, the Earth tilts on its axis towards the Sun. This has two effects:

a) The periods of daylight are longer and so more warming. The nights are shorter and so less cooling.

b) Because the Earth is tilted towards the Sun, the heat radiation is more intense (concentrated into a smaller surface area) in summer, so the heating effect is greater: the Sun seems hotter. Some children think that summer and winter are caused by the Earth moving closer to or further from the Sun in its orbit. However, this difference is negligible compared to the 150 million kilometres distance between the Earth and the Sun.

Answers
1. 15°C
2. The air in the room was at 25°C, but the temperature of human blood is 37°C. The temperature of a human hand is just a few degrees below blood temperature.
3. The classroom was probably warmer than the outside because it was a sunny day and the windows were letting in radiated heat from the Sun, but only two windows were open to let in cooler air. The difference in temperature could also have been due to the body heat of the people in the room.
4. Summer
5. The sunlight passed through the glass in the window and heated the water.
6. Around 15°C (this is the temperature of the water from the cold tap, which comes from the ground – at night, the air temperature would be similar).

How hot is it?

A group of children were exploring the temperature at various places in and near their classroom, using a datalogger fitted with a temperature sensor. The classroom had only two windows open.

The children recorded their results in a bar graph.

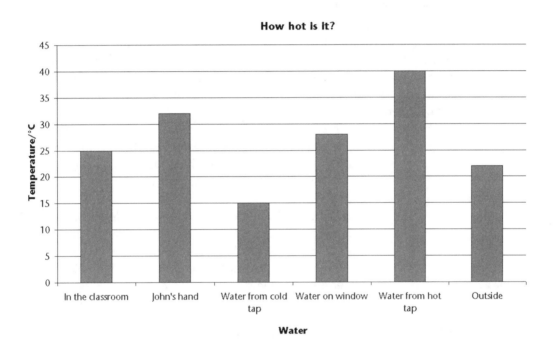

How hot is It?

Temperature/°C (vertical axis, 0 to 45)

Categories: In the classroom, John's hand, Water from cold tap, Water on window, Water from hot tap, Outside

Water (horizontal axis label)

Questions

1. What was the lowest temperature that the children recorded?

2. Why was the temperature of John's hand higher than the temperature of the room?

3. Why was the temperature in the classroom higher than the temperature outside?

4. The temperature outside was 23°C. What season of the year do you think it was?

5. The temperature of the water that had been left on the window was much higher than the temperature of the water straight from the cold tap. Explain why.

6. Predict what the temperature of the classroom will be later that night.

LOOKING AT THE WEATHER

> *National Curriculum Science* KS2 PoS Sc1: 2i, j; Sc3: 2c
> *QCA Science* Unit 4C: Keeping warm
> *Scottish 5–14 Guidelines* Earth in space – Level B

HOW TO GATHER THE DATA

In the English National Curriculum, Sc1 (Scientific enquiry) promotes the use of secondary sources of data. Children will enjoy exploring the Met Office website (www.metoffice.com); they can obtain lots of data from the weather station nearest to their home, compare the weather with other parts of the country, and use e-mail to set up links with other schools.

THE SCIENCE BEHIND THE DATA

It is important that children relate making measurements of temperature in the classroom to the measurements made in the context of weather recording. The scientists who work at the many Met Office sites around the UK need to measure the maximum and minimum temperatures each day, the number of hours of sunshine, the amount of rainfall and the wind speed and direction. Discussing the importance of these data can form a valuable cross-curricular link between science and geography.

Weather data can be used to focus on environmental issues. For example, recent data have shown that October 2001 was the warmest October in the UK since 1642. The evidence of global warming and its long-term implications can be discussed with the children.

You can use a large globe and a torch to demonstrate how the Earth's northern hemisphere tilts towards the Sun in the summer and tilts away from the Sun in the winter. Point out how the torchlight is more intense when it is spread over a smaller area. Simple diagrams (see below) can help to make this point. You can use this to explain the temperate climate of the northern hemisphere with its four seasons, referring to the pattern of temperatures and hours of sunshine recorded through the year. The familiar features of summer and winter in our climate are caused by the Earth's tilt. The familiar biological features of spring and autumn are caused by the life cycles of deciduous trees, which grow leaves in the spring and lose them in the autumn.

Answers

1. July.
2. January, February, December.
3. 16°C
4. 14°C
5. 62mm
6. December.
7. 21mm
8. July, because the weather is at its warmest and the rainfall is only at an average level.
9. You would expect the rainfall to be higher in the winter months, whereas the maximum temperatures would occur in the summer when the Sun is close to its highest position in the sky above the UK.
10. There does not seem to be a clear pattern, except that the rainfall is higher between November and January than in the rest of the year.
11. The average maximum temperature rises from January to July where it reaches a peak, then decreases from July to December.
12. Yes. The northern hemisphere of the Earth is tilted towards the Sun in the summer, and so the Sun appears to be higher in the sky and the UK has higher temperatures. In the winter the northern hemisphere is tilted away from the Sun, so the temperatures in the UK are lower.

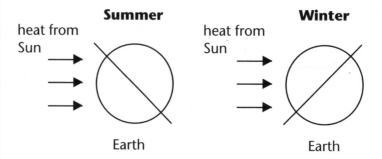

Looking at the weather

A class of children in Shawpool, a small village near Shrewsbury, decided to investigate what the weather had been like in their village over the last 30 years. They downloaded the data on temperatures from the Met Office website www.metoffice.com and plotted it as a bar graph. Their graph showed the average temperature for each month over the last 30 years.

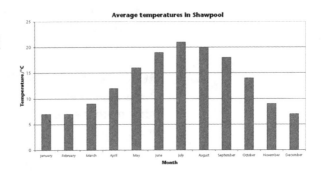

Questions

1. Which was the hottest month of the year?

2. Which were the coldest months of the year?

3. What was the average temperature recorded in May?

4. What was the difference in average temperature between the coldest month and the hottest month?

Then the children looked at the rainfall figures. They plotted a bar graph to show the average rainfall for each month over the last 30 years.

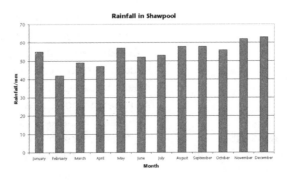

5. How many millimetres of rain fell, on average, in November?

6. In which month was the greatest average rainfall measured?

7. What was the difference in average rainfall between the driest month and the wettest month?

8. A group of children from Iceland want to visit this school when there is good weather. Look at the data on temperature and rainfall. When would you advise them to visit? Give them two reasons.

9. Why do you think the month with the highest maximum temperature is not the month when there is the highest rainfall?

10. What can you say about the overall pattern of rainfall in Shawpool from looking at the second graph?

11. What can you say about the overall pattern of temperatures in Shawpool from looking at the first graph?

12. Would you expect this pattern of temperatures? Why?

KEEPING YOUR LOLLY COLD

National Curriculum Science KS2 PoS Sc3: 1b, 2c
QCA Science Unit 4C: Keeping warm
Scottish 5–14 Guidelines Materials from Earth – Level B; Properties and uses of energy – Level D

HOW TO GATHER THE DATA

This is a good example of an investigation where datalogging is superior to other methods (such as the use of a thermometer) for collecting the data, since:

■ It provides a numerical readout.
■ You can set it up and come back later when it is finished.
■ You do not have to write out lots of readings.
■ If a thermometer is inside another object, you cannot see the scale.

A datalogger with an extension lead to a temperature sensor is best for this activity. The lollies need to be taken straight from the freezer and wrapped before they can melt.

THE SCIENCE BEHIND THE DATA

When the particles in a material are heated, they gain energy and move more vigorously. They can vibrate more (in a solid) or move from one place to another more quickly (in a liquid or gas). Heat can be transferred from one place to another in three different ways:

1. Conduction – the particles vibrate rapidly and pass on the vibrations to the particles next to them, which pass them on further. Metals are good conductors of heat, because their electrons can move freely, passing the energy with them. Non-metals and liquids are poor conductors. Gases are very poor conductors because their particles are so far apart. Conduction cannot take place through a vacuum, since there are no particles.

2. Convection – this happens in liquids and gases, where the particles are free to move around. When they are heated, the particles move more vigorously and spread out, carrying energy with them. As a result, the density becomes less and the warmer liquid or gas will rise. Many children say that heat rises, but in fact the heat itself cannot rise: the hot liquid or gas rises and carries the energy with it.

3. Radiation – all objects give out infra-red radiation. Very hot objects, such as a light bulb filament, give out visible light as well. Radiation does not require other particles to be there. It can travel across the near-vacuum of space from the Sun. Shiny surfaces are the poorest radiators; dark, dull surfaces are the best radiators. The same applies to absorbing radiation: dark colours absorb heat more than light colours. Try wearing a black T-shirt on a hot day!

Answers

1. The bubble wrap.
2. The plastic bag.
3. The air in the room was warmer than the frozen lollies – the lollies absorb this heat.
4. Between 12 and 13 minutes.
5. It began to melt.
6. When the temperature of an ice lolly is above 0°C it will melt, since that is the melting point of ice.
7. Bubble wrap. (This question will highlight whether or not the children understand a negative scale.)
8. Bubble wrap –1.3°C, paper towel –0.2°C, plastic bag 1.0°C.
9. The bubble wrap.
10. The lolly is kept cold because the bubble wrap stops the heat getting in. It will not let the heat pass through it easily. Therefore, it would also stop the heat getting out from a warm object.

Keeping your lolly cold

Molly and Alistair wanted to keep their ice lollies cold to stop them from melting. They tried wrapping a lolly in each of three different materials, and attached a datalogger temperature sensor to each one so they could measure the changes in its temperature over a period of time.

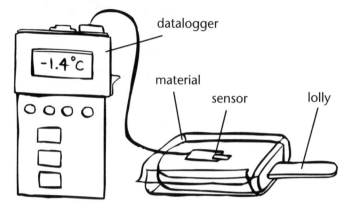

This is the graph from the datalogger. It shows how the temperature of the three ice lollies changed with time.

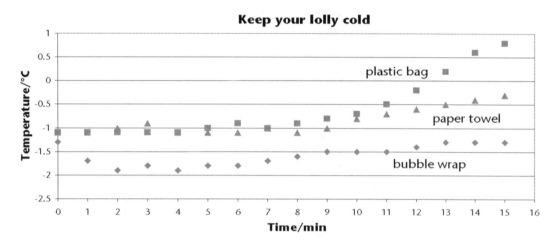

Questions

1. Which material was best for keeping the lolly cold?

2. Which material let the lolly warm up the most?

3. Why do you think the temperature of all three lollies increased over 15 minutes?

4. How long did it take for the lolly in the plastic bag to reach 0°C?

5. What do you think happened to the lolly in the plastic bag after that?

6. Use science to explain your answer to Question 5.

7. The reading on the datalogger in the picture above was taken at 12 minutes. What was the lolly wrapped in?

8. Draw in what you predict the next temperature reading will be, at 16 minutes, for each material.

9. Which wrapping do you think would be the best for keeping things warm?

10. Use science to explain your answer to Question 9.

HANDLING SCIENCE DATA YEAR 4

KEEPING BAKED POTATOES HOT

> *National Curriculum Science* KS2 PoS Sc3: 1a, b; 2c
> *QCA Science* Unit 4C: Keeping warm
> *Scottish 5–14 Guidelines* Materials from Earth – Level B

HOW TO GATHER THE DATA

If you have a microwave oven or a normal oven in the classroom, then this investigation can be carried out easily. Remember to use two potatoes of equal size, and to place the temperature probe in the centre of each potato. (In the data presented opposite, the start temperatures have been equalised for simplicity, but the real difference was negligible.) One advantage of datalogging in this activity is that the children do not have to unwrap the potato to take readings. If you are displaying the data on a screen, the children can identify trends and make predictions.

THE SCIENCE BEHIND THE DATA

This activity demonstrates to children that datalogging can be used to find the answers to real-life questions. The idea that the potato will cool to room temperature and not below that level is difficult for many children. Leave the datalogger on for a long time and the children will see the temperature level off. If you also measure the temperature of the room, they have evidence that this is the level to which the potato has cooled. Ask them to predict the final temperature in a number of similar cooling experiments, encouraging them to refine their ideas. Ask questions such as: *If the potato starts off colder than the room, what will happen to it then?* Someone will say that the potato will take in heat from the room and become warmer. Some children may even suggest (though not necessarily in these words) that the temperature of a potato at room temperature stays constant because the heat is going into the potato from the room at the same rate that it is being lost from the potato to the room.

As the potato cools, it loses heat through radiation and convection. The hot potato radiates more heat than it absorbs from other radiating sources (such as the Sun or a light bulb). Also, because the surface of the potato is hotter than the surrounding air, it loses energy to it: air particles hit the surface and gain energy, so they move more quickly, taking energy away from the surface. These are continuous processes, so they happen at a steady rate. The shiny aluminium is a poor radiator of heat, so it reduces the rate of heat loss more effectively than the paper wrapper (which lets radiated heat through).

Answers

1. 93°C
2. 30°C
3. 43°C
4. 13°C
5. 82°C
6. After 12 minutes.
7. It will be slightly hotter than the baked potato wrapped in paper, and so will taste better.
8. Ask a number of people to taste samples of the two baked potatoes and see which they prefer.
9. The aluminium foil keeps the potato hotter because it radiates less heat from the potato. The paper bag is more permeable and is a better radiator of heat.
10. The surface of the potato is warmer than its surroundings. This means that it loses heat by warming up the air particles that hit the potato surface, as well as by radiating heat into the surroundings. These processes continue as long as the potato is warmer than its surroundings, so they happen at a steady rate.
11. The temperature of the room.

Keeping baked potatoes hot

Indira wondered why the take away shop wrapped their baked potatoes in aluminium foil, rather than in paper like fish and chips. She decided to investigate the effect of using each wrapping material. She cooked two baked potatoes together in a microwave for five minutes. Afterwards, she wrapped one in paper and the other in aluminium foil. She put a temperature probe in each potato and recorded the temperature over a period of 30 minutes.

Her graph looked like this:

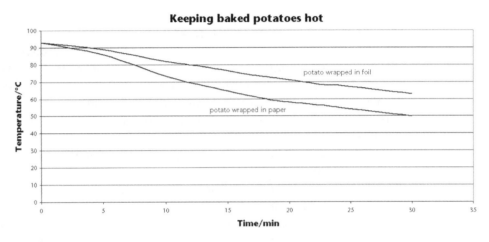

Questions

1. What was the temperature of both potatoes when Indira first inserted the probes?

2. How much did the temperature of the baked potato wrapped in foil fall by in half an hour?

3. How much did the temperature of the baked potato wrapped in paper fall by in half an hour?

4. What is the difference between the two final temperatures?

5. What was the temperature of the baked potato in foil after 10 minutes?

6. After how much time was the temperature of the baked potato wrapped in paper 70°C?

7. Most people collecting a baked potato from a take away shop would probably eat it within 10 minutes – so why is it better to wrap it in foil?

8. How could you test whether the temperature of a potato affects the taste?

9. Can you explain why foil wrapping keeps the potato hotter than paper wrapping does?

10. The temperature in both cases seems to fall at a steady rate. Can you explain why?

11. What will the temperature of both potatoes be the same as after 2 hours?

HANDLING SCIENCE DATA YEAR 4

CLASSIFYING MATERIALS

National Curriculum Science KS2 PoS Sc3: 1e
QCA Science Unit 4D: Solids, liquids and how they can be separated
Scottish 5–14 Guidelines Materials from Earth – Level C

HOW TO GATHER THE DATA

Offer the children some straightforward examples to start with, then introduce some that can stimulate a debate (such as Plasticine, soap bubbles or icing sugar).

THE SCIENCE BEHIND THE DATA

Children often have difficulty with the idea of **properties** of materials. It can be teased out from them using the distinction between an **object** (what it is), a **material** (what it is made from) and a **property** (what it is like). For example: *A table (object) is made from wood (material), which is hard (property).*

The definitions that we normally use for the properties of a solid, a liquid and a gas are:

- A **solid** has a fixed shape and a fixed volume, and is hard to compress.
- A **liquid** takes the shape of the container it is in, has a fixed volume and is hard to compress.
- A **gas** takes the shape of all the space available, has no fixed volume and is easy to compress (but compressing it gets harder as its pressure increases).

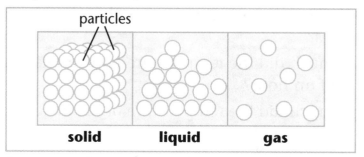

The properties described above will only apply in all cases to pure substances. Children may suggest other properties – for example: 'Solids are hard' or 'Liquids flow.' These are problematic: not all solids are hard (rubber is soft), and solid powders (such as sand) can flow. Sand flows because the sand grains can move past each other, as the particles of a liquid do (but the latter are much, much smaller). A block of sandstone will not flow.

Other difficulties arise when mixtures are considered – for example, foam retains its shape for a while, but is not a solid: it is a mixture of gas and liquid. Smoke is a very finely divided solid in a gas (which is why it can leave a solid residue on walls). Mist or fog is fine droplets of liquid in a gas. Plasticine and unbaked clay are mixtures of a solid and a liquid.

A difficult question we have been asked is: 'If a solid dissolves, does it become a liquid?' The answer is no, because the solid is not melting. A different thing is happening: the solid particles are separating and being carried with the liquid, so the result is a mixture of a solid and a liquid.

Answers

1. T-shirt and candle = solid, orange juice = liquid. Smoke is a mixture of a solid and a gas (see notes above), so 'unsure' is a fair answer. The answer 'gas' or 'solid' alone is incomplete, but you may decide to accept it for this age group.

2. Solids.

3. Probably yes (in most classrooms).

4. Liquids do not have a fixed shape/they are runny/they would flow/they would spill all over!

5. The liquid would take the shape of the bowl, because liquids have no fixed shape. The volume of each liquid would not change.

6. Gases.

7. Gases in the air such as nitrogen (also in crisp packets), oxygen, hydrogen, carbon dioxide, helium, argon (also in light bulbs) and neon. Fuel gases such as methane (in gas pipes and heaters), propane (stored as liquid in red cylinders) and butane (stored as liquid in blue cylinders and lighters).

8. Sand and flour can flow, but they are solids. Plasticine can be made into new shapes – it is a mixture of a solid and a liquid. Judge the reasoning behind the child's decision, rather than the decision alone.

9. See the definitions above. Accept any sensible suggestions.

Classifying materials

Miss Williams brought in some objects for Class 4 to look at. She had three hoops. She asked the children to put the solid materials in one hoop, the liquid materials in another hoop, and the materials that were gases in the third hoop. They could overlap the hoops for objects that belonged in more than one hoop. Any objects they were unsure of were left on the carpet.

The class drew up this table of their results on the board.

Solids	Liquids	Gases	Unsure
Football	Water	Air in football	Sand
Teddy bear	Cola	Air in balloon	Flour
Photo frame	Oil	Fizzy gas in cola	Plasticine
Banana	Milk		
Sunglasses			
Metal teapot			
Red toy car			
Bright pink tights			
Pineapple			
Balloon (flat)			

Questions

1. Add these other objects to the table: T-shirt, candle, orange juice, smoke.

2. Which type of objects form the largest group?

3. Do these form the largest group of objects in your classroom?

4. All the liquids were kept in containers (beakers). Why?

5. What would happen if we put the liquids into bowls? Explain why. Would the volume of each liquid change?

6. Which type of objects formed the smallest group (not counting 'Unsure')?

7. Can you think of any other objects that would go in this group? Add them to the table.

8. Class 4 were unsure which group to put sand, flour and Plasticine in. Why do you think they were unsure? Which group would you put them in?

9. If you had to describe the properties of solids, liquids and gases to another Year 4 class, how would you do it?

THICK AND THIN LIQUIDS

National Curriculum Science KS2 PoS Sc3: 1e
QCA Science Unit 4D: Solids, liquids and how they can be separated
Scottish 5–14 Guidelines Materials from Earth – Level C

HOW TO GATHER THE DATA

You will need to obtain a number of empty washing-up liquid bottles, one for each group of children. Cut the bottoms off the bottles, and make sure that no liquid can leak out anywhere when you hold your finger over the hole. Choose a range of liquids of different 'thicknesses'. It is best to leave the oil to the end, because it is harder to clean up. Children can measure out 100cm^3 of each liquid into a beaker or measuring cylinder. One child can hold the washing-up bottle with a finger securely over the hole while another child operates the stopwatch. Pour the measured liquid into the washing-up liquid bottle, then uncover the hole and start the stopwatch. The children will need to decide when the thicker liquids have stopped flowing – in the tests shown here, we decided it was when continuous flow ended. However, some materials (such as syrup and tomato ketchup) may be difficult to test using this method, or may have to be done as a demonstration over several hours. Thicker liquids will drip rather than form a continuous stream. (Tomato sauce took 75 minutes to drip through in our investigation.)

Before the children carry out the tests, ask them to predict which materials are liquids. Are there any they are not sure about? Review this with the children after the test, asking them why they think the materials are liquids. The test can also be used to demonstrate that powders are not liquids: apart from a few particles at first, a powder will not flow through a narrow hole unless it is tapped strongly.

THE SCIENCE BEHIND THE DATA

Research (Driver et al, 1994) and our experience of working with children in classrooms have shown that most children describe liquids as 'runny', 'watery' or 'something that pours'. They can identify water as a liquid, and most of the liquids they experience (such as fizzy drinks, squash and milk) have a water base. It is important to use this investigation to reinforce the idea that many other materials used in everyday life (such as oil, bubble bath mixture, shampoo, tomato ketchup and honey) are also liquids: even though they are much thicker (more viscous) than the watery liquids, and so resist flow, they still have the property of flowing and will change shape in different containers. Viscous liquids tend to be made up of complex molecules, either tangled together (as in oil) or suspended in water (as in honey or shampoo).

Answers

1. Water and milk.
2. Yes: they are both thin, watery liquids.
3. Bubble bath.
4. 77 seconds.
5. Because bubble bath mixture is very thick, being made of detergent.
6. 46 seconds.
7. 70 seconds.
8. Answers roughly halfway between 7 seconds (water) and 25 seconds (washing-up liquid) are acceptable: approximately 16 seconds.
9. Yes: only a liquid would all flow down through a hole in this way.
10. Children may suggest a range of other liquids: fizzy drinks, orange juice, petrol, tar, warm custard, honey and so on.
11. Answers over 30 minutes would be acceptable. Look for an understanding that it would take much longer than the materials shown in the graph.
12. Yes, because it will flow (run) or drip.

Thick and thin liquids

Hannah, Rani and Jon knew that water was a liquid. They weren't sure whether some things they used at home, such as bubble bath and cooking oil, were liquids. Hannah said that liquids can flow. They decided to test whether the materials were liquids by seeing how fast they flowed.

They took a washing-up bottle, cut off the bottom and turned the bottle upside down. They poured 100cm³ of the material into the bottle and measured how long it took for the material to run through the hole in the bottom.

The children plotted their results on a bar graph.

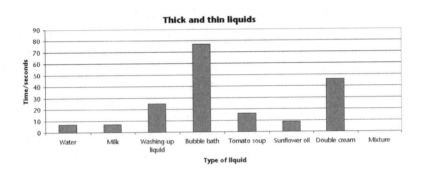

Questions

1. Name the two liquids that flowed most easily through the hole in the bottle.

2. Would you expect these liquids to take the same time to flow through the hole? Why?

3. Which liquid took the longest time to flow through the hole in the bottle?

4. How long did it take?

5. Why do you think it took the longest time of all the liquids?

6. How many seconds did it take the double cream to flow through the hole?

7. How many more seconds did it take the bubble bath to flow through the hole than the water?

8. Rani made a mixture from 50cm³ of water and 50cm³ of washing-up liquid. How long do you predict it will take to flow through the hole? Draw your prediction on the bar chart where it says 'Mixture'.

9. At the start, Hannah, Rani and Jon weren't sure which materials were liquids. All the materials they tested flowed through the hole. Do you think they were all liquids?

10. Are there any other materials that you could test in this way to find out whether they are liquids?

11. Predict how long tomato sauce would take to pass through the hole.

12. Do you think tomato sauce is a liquid? Explain your answer.

DISSOLVING SUGAR

National Curriculum Science KS2 PoS Sc3: 2a, 3b
QCA Science Unit 4D: Solids, liquids and how they can be separated
Scottish 5–14 Guidelines Changing materials – Level B

HOW TO GATHER THE DATA

The children need to have some experience of different sugars before attempting this activity. Initially, show the children the different types of sugar and ask them to predict which sugar will dissolve first. Encourage them to give a reason for their prediction. You can give each group of children a magnifying glass to help them observe closely and evaluate their predictions. They can use hand-hot water and stirring to reduce the dissolving time.

THE SCIENCE BEHIND THE DATA

For a solid to dissolve in water (or another liquid), the energy input needed to break down the solid crystals needs to be less than the energy output released when the solution is formed. Even when this is the case, the solid will only dissolve when the energy input is provided. This is why using warmer water helps to dissolve a solid. Sugar crystals of a smaller size dissolve faster because more solid surface is exposed for the same amount of sugar, so the sugar particles mix more readily with the water particles. Stirring speeds up the rate of dissolving because it disperses the solid particles among the water particles.

This investigation could form part of a series of practical activities on dissolving. The first activity might look at four materials, such as sand, sugar, salt and flour, in order to establish that some materials (such as salt and sugar) are soluble in water while other materials (such as sand and flour) are insoluble. Explore the children's ideas on how to make materials dissolve – salt and sugar dissolve only very slowly in cold water unless they are stirred. A further activity could explore the effect of stirring and temperature on dissolving. A final activity could look at the effect of particle size on dissolving. This can be related to other contexts – why are some medicines sold as powders instead of tablets?

Some insoluble substances can mislead children: flour contains very fine particles, which form a milky suspension when stirred with water. However, the flour will settle out if left. It is also important for the children to distinguish between 'white' and 'colourless' – the latter word being used to describe water and solutions of salt or sugar. The effect of a solid powder on the appearance of a liquid will depend on whether the solid dissolves:

■ A white solid that is soluble (such as salt) will give a colourless, transparent solution. Note that colourless and transparent are two different properties: children often use them interchangably.

■ A white insoluble solid will give a white, non-transparent suspension, such as milk.

■ A coloured soluble solid gives a same-coloured and transparent solution, such as coffee.

■ A coloured insoluble solid will give a coloured suspension (such as powder paint), or settle as a coloured sediment (such as sand) and leave the water colourless.

Answers

1. Icing sugar.
2. 5.5 seconds.
3. Granulated sugar has larger pieces (particles, crystals) than the other types of sugar, so it takes longer to break down.
4. The sugar would take longer to dissolve in cold water. (Encourage the children to make full statements, rather than just saying 'It would be slower'. Watch out for non-answer responses such as 'It will sink to the bottom.')
5. The dissolving time would be longer if the water were not stirred.
6. The dissolving time would be longer with only 5cm³ of water, or the sugar might not all dissolve. (This is an open-ended question, so allow any sensible suggestions.)
7. Same amount of sugar (1 teaspoon), same amount of water (100cm³), same temperature (50°C), same number of stirs (five).
8. Any time longer than for granulated sugar (relate the quality of the estimate to the ability of the child).
9. The sugar cubes are much larger than the grains of granulated sugar, so it takes longer for them to break down.

Dissolving sugar

Mark, Kerry and Bashir decided to investigate how long it took for different types of sugar to dissolve. They added 1 teaspoon of sugar to 100cm³ of warm water (at 50°C) and stirred five times. They measured the amount of time it took the sugar to dissolve using a stopwatch, and recorded their results in a bar graph.

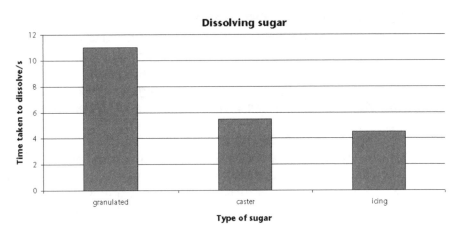

Questions

1. Which type of sugar dissolved the fastest?

2. How long did it take for the caster sugar to dissolve?

The children examined each type of sugar and commented:
- "This granulated sugar is like what I put on my cornflakes, it's all gritty," said Kerry.
- "The caster sugar is like that, but smaller crystals," said Bashir.
- Mark said, 'The icing sugar is all powdery."

3. Why do you think the granulated sugar took the longest time to dissolve? Think about how the children described the different types of sugar.

4. Suppose the children used cold water. Do you think the sugar would dissolve more quickly or more slowly, or would it be just the same?

5. What do you think would have happened to the dissolving time if the children had not stirred the water?

6. What do you think would have happened in the investigation if the children had only used a small amount of water (say 5cm³) for the same amount of sugar?

7. What did Mark, Kerry and Bashir keep the same to make their investigation fair?

8. You can buy sugar in cubes that are 1cm³ in size. How long do you think it would take one of these sugar cubes to dissolve in water at 50°C?

9. Explain your answer to Question 8.

CAR RAMPS

> ***National Curriculum Science*** KS2 PoS Sc4: 2c
> ***QCA Science*** Unit 4E: Friction
> ***Scottish 5–14 Guidelines*** Forces and their effects – Level A, B, C, D

HOW TO GATHER THE DATA

The children can measure the distance travelled using a tape measure, or even a roll of paper – till roll can be cut to the distance travelled by each car and used to make a display chart. The exercise can be turned the other way round by trying to get the car to finish at a given target distance. The diagram on page 64 shows how to make a cheap, adjustable ramp from 'corroflute'.

THE SCIENCE BEHIND THE DATA

Gravity pulls the car down the ramp, causing it to speed up all the time it is on the ramp. The longer the time that gravity is acting on the car, the more the car will speed up in its forward movement – so the car travelling from a greater height will be travelling faster, and thus will travel further when it reaches the ground. Friction between the surface of the ramp and the car's wheels, and between the axles and the wheels, will slow the car down. The greater the friction, the shorter the distance travelled by the car.

Friction, drag and air resistance are all forces that oppose the movement of an object, slowing it down. They only operate when the object is moving – when an object is moving it has momentum. The action of these forces can be explained in terms of the transfer of momentum from the moving object to the surface (such as a carpet, water or air) across which the object is moving.

For example, consider the movement of a brick across a carpet. As the brick moves, the fibres in the carpet are pushed down and sideways, so the bick loses some of its momentum to the carpet, which gains this momentum. Any particles in any surface will act in a similar way, but you cannot always see this happening. A rough surface has more points that will 'snag' and retard the movement; on a smoother surface there are fewer such points, so objects can slide along it more easily.

Many factors can affect friction, however, so it is not easy to predict which surfaces will have the most friction. Friction depends upon the effect of two surfaces on each other and the downward force pressing these two surfaces together. Also, it is harder to start an object moving against 'static' friction than to keep it moving against 'dynamic' friction (which is a lesser force). The children may notice this if they pull a heavy object across a surface.

Answers

1. Yes.
2. The child might push some cars slightly harder than others, and so they would go further.
3. Any two of: don't push the cars; start the cars at the same position on the ramp; use the same height of ramp and starting point; measure the distance to the same place on the car.
4. Bar graph:

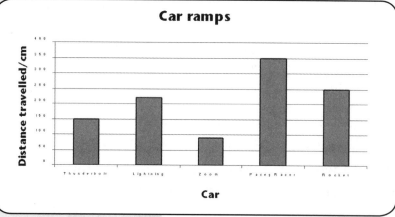

5. Pacey Racer.
6. Zoom.
7. Thunderbolt, Lightning.
8. Cars drawn in appropriate positions in the order (left to right): Zoom, Thunderbolt, Lightning, Rocket, Pacey Racer.
9. Friction. The child may suggest air resistance, but this is minimal compared to friction with the floor surface.
10. Zoom.
11. This car travelled the shortest distance.

Car ramps

The class had been making some cars in technology, and they wanted to see whose car would travel the furthest. Simon wanted to test this by pushing each car. Ranjit said that would not be a fair test.

Questions

1. Is Ranjit right when he says that pushing the cars would not be a fair test?

2. Explain your answer to Question 1.

The children decided to let the cars roll down a ramp and measure how far each car went. This is how they did the test.

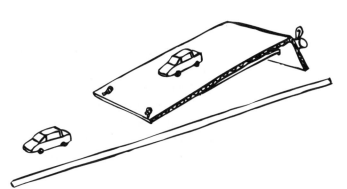

3. What two things should they have done to make sure the test was fair?

Here are the children's results.

4. Plot the results as a bar graph.

5. Which car travelled the furthest?

6. Which car travelled the least distance?

7. Name the two cars drawn below.

8. Draw on the other cars in the positions where they finished.

Car	Distance travelled/cm
Thunderbolt	150
Lightning	220
Zoom	90
Pacey Racer	350
Rocket	250

start

0 start   1m   2m   3m   4m

0   1m   2m   3m   4m

9. What is the name of the force that slows the car down?

10. Which car had the greatest 'slowing' force?

11. Explain how you can tell this from the results.

A HEAVY BOX

National Curriculum Science KS2 PoS Sc4: 2c, e
QCA Science Unit 4E: Friction
Scottish 5–14 Guidelines Forces and their effects – Levels A, B, C

HOW TO GATHER THE DATA

This is a good extension activity for more able children. The investigation requires careful measurement of the pulling force, good ability to devise and use a table for data, and an intuitive understanding of the idea that friction is affected by mass.

THE SCIENCE BEHIND THE DATA

Friction can be treated in a relatively simple way (as here); but you should be aware, when looking at results, that many complex factors can affect the friction between two surfaces. The amount of friction force depends on the interaction between the two surfaces (called the coefficient of friction) and the downward force pressing the object onto the surface. It does not depend on the area of contact. For example, if you double the area of the bottom of the box, you also halve the pressure caused by a given mass, so the two effects cancel out. However, increasing the mass in the box increases the downward force acting on the same area, so the friction force increases.

If the children's understanding has developed far enough, the investigation can be used to illustrate four distinct principles of scientific experiments:

1. Fair testing – keeping things that would affect the result the same, apart from those you intend to vary. The measuring instrument and masses used do not need to be the same, because they depend on standard units.

2. Reliability – are the results repeatable? If we repeat the same test several times and get the same results every time, we can say the test is reliable.

3. Accuracy – does the measuring instrument give correct readings? A home-made force meter using an elastic band is not as accurate as a commercial force meter.

4. Precision – this depends on how finely your measuring instrument is calibrated. A 0–10N force meter measuring to the nearest 1N is more precise than a 0–100N force meter that only goes up in 10N divisions.

Describing the trend of a graph is something that children may need support with. Teachers often find that children know what the trend of a set of data is, but cannot find a way of expressing it. We have found that making it into a simple rhythm or jingle provides a scaffold on which they can structure their response: *The greater the mass, the harder the pull.* The first line describes what you have changed; the second line describes what you have measured. The sentence can be read with a rhythm rather like that of an old-fashioned train on a track. Having this support helps the children to focus on the essentials of the investigation and not wander off into a long-winded, complex expression of their ideas. It is thus very helpful in developing clear and concise thinking and expression.

Answers

1. a) 6N **b)** 7N
2. 200g and 700g
3. These results do not seem to fit the overall trend: the result for 200g is too high and the result for 700g is too low.
4. 4N and 9N
5. The bar should have a height of 12N.
6. 6.5N
7. The greater the mass contained in the box, the greater the force needed to pull the box. (Encourage full statements like this. Discourage incomplete statements such as 'It gets bigger' – see 'The science behind the data' above.)
8. Same box, same surface. (Not the same newtonmeter or masses, as these are standard.)
9. The box has some mass, or a force is needed to move the box anyway. The first answer is preferable.

A heavy box

Mei Tin and Chi Kin thought that a heavier box would be harder to pull than a lighter one. They put weights in a wooden box to see whether that changed the pulling force needed to move the box. They added another 100g each time.

Here is a bar graph of the children's results.

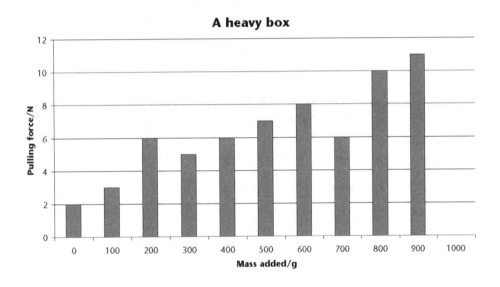

Questions

1. What pulling force is needed for **a)** 400g **b)** 500g?

2. Which two results do you think the children should check again?

3. Explain how you decided this.

4. What results would you expect the children to get if they tried with those two masses again?

5. Draw a bar to predict the result for 1000g.

6. What would you expect the result to be if they tried 450g?

7. How does the amount of mass added to the box affect the force needed to pull it?

8. Name two things the children should do to make their investigation a fair test.

9. Why is the pulling force needed more than zero even when there are no weights in the box?

HANDLING SCIENCE DATA YEAR 4

FRICTION ON DIFFERENT SURFACES

National Curriculum Science KS2 PoS Sc4: 2c, e
QCA Science Unit 4E: Friction
Scottish 5–14 Guidelines Forces and their effects – Levels B, C

HOW TO GATHER THE DATA

It is easy to set up this investigation with groups of children in a class. Boards covered with different materials can be bought from primary science suppliers, or made by an adult. It is important to position each board so that the end overlaps the edge of the desk. You will need a number of plastic margarine tubs or similar, and a number of 10g and 100g masses. Alternatively, the investigation could be carried out by using a force meter to pull the block along the surfaces.

You can use this investigation to encourage children's measuring skills: they need to measure out and mark the 40cm distance between the starting and finishing lines accurately on each surface.

Answers

1. 500g
2. 70g
3. 430g
4. The wooden surface (no covering).
5. Because they realised that there might be slight errors, so they could get a more reliable result by repeating the measurements and taking the average.
6. Discuss the reasons with the children. The reasons might include slightly different positions of the block on the start line or the finish line.
7. To find the average, the children added the two measurements together and divided by 2.
8. Mass of wooden block, distance between start and finish line, length of string, position of block on the start and finish lines.
9. The sandpaper was the roughest (most uneven) surface, so there was more friction between it and the block.
10. The wooden surface was very smooth, so there was very little friction between it and the block.
11. Accept answers significantly lower than 65g – ideally around 40g.
12. The oil will act as a lubricant, reducing the friction even more.

THE SCIENCE BEHIND THE DATA

Show the children examples of the different surfaces. Allow them to feel each surface and use a magnifying glass to examine it more closely. Ask them to predict on which surface the wooden block will slide most easily. Effectively, the masses placed inside the tub are measuring the force required to make the block move.

Ask the children to observe what happens when the block starts to move: it will suddenly start to move fast, rather than speed up gradually. It takes more force to start an object moving (against 'static friction') than to keep it moving (against 'dynamic friction').

Friction depends on the 'snagging' of molecules between surfaces that are in contact. The wood and plastic surfaces used in the investigation were smooth, so there was very little friction between these and the block. The carpet had a fairly even pile, so again there was a small amount of friction. However, the sandpaper surface was rough and bumpy, so the friction between it and the block was comparatively large. The force needed to overcome the static friction in this case was approximately 5N, since a mass of 500g was needed. The force applied can be calculated (in N) as the product of the mass (in kg) and the strength of gravity (almost 10N/kg).

Ask the children to draw a diagram of the forces. They should show the friction force acting in the opposite direction to the pulling force exerted by the masses in the tub. It is also important to explore with them the idea that there are forces acting on the block before it starts moving: gravity and the upthrust of the surface. Many children think that no forces act on an object when it is not moving (see Driver, R et al, 1994).

Friction on different surfaces

A group of children investigated how movement was affected by using different surfaces. They used wooden boards covered with different materials: sandpaper, smooth plastic, carpet and wood (no covering). They marked a start line and a finish line 40cm apart on each board. They placed a wooden block on the start line and connected it to a tub with string. They put masses in the tub until the block moved to the finish line. They repeated their tests and worked out the average mass needed to move the block from start to finish.

They recorded the results in a table, then a bar graph.

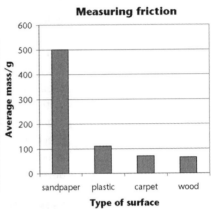

Surface	Mass to move block/g		Average mass to move block/g
	1st try	2nd try	
Sandpaper	500	500	500
Plastic	100	120	110
Carpet	70	70	70
Wood	60	70	65

Questions

1. What was the average mass needed to move the block on the sandpaper?

2. What was the average mass needed to move the block on the carpet?

3. How much more mass was needed to move the wooden block on the sandpaper than on the carpet?

4. Which surface required the smallest mass to make the wooden block move from the start line to the finish line?

5. Why did the children repeat their measurements?

6. Why do you think some of the measurements the children made were slightly different the second time?

7. How did they calculate the average mass required to make the block move on each surface?

8. What things did the children need to keep the same in their investigation?

9. Why do you think the largest mass was needed to move the block on the sandpaper?

10. Why do you think the smallest mass was needed to move the block on the wooden surface?

11. If you coated the wooden board with oil, what mass do you predict would be needed to make the block move?

12. Explain your prediction.

HANDLING SCIENCE DATA YEAR 4

PARACHUTES

National Curriculum Science KS2 PoS Sc4: 2c
QCA Science Unit 4E: Friction
Scottish 5–14 Guidelines Forces and their effects – Level C

HOW TO GATHER THE DATA

Parachutes provide a rich opportunity for investigative work, since there are so many factors that can be tested. To compare falling times within the classroom, you will need stopwatches or timers that measure to 0.01s. Depending on the children's numeracy skills, they can either try to record the decimal numbers or ignore the decimal point and just record the digits.

This investigation is a good exercise in co-ordination and teamwork. The children need to start and stop the watch at exactly the right times, and this will require a clear method and allocation of roles (for example: one person to drop the parachute, another to say '3–2–1–Go', a third to start and stop the watch and a fourth to record the result). The children's timing will become more reliable with practice. Emphasise the importance of having a consistent procedure. The higher they can hold the parachute at the start, the better (ideally at least 3m) – but this needs to be done safely. The children should discard unreliable results – for example, if a parachute does not open properly.

THE SCIENCE BEHIND THE DATA

The children may observe that the parachute speeds up when it is first released (before it opens), and then travels at a steady speed until it hits the floor. At the start, the parachute accelerates under the influence of gravity. When the parachute opens out, the air resistance acting on it increases. The faster the parachute falls, the greater the air resistance is, so the acceleration decreases until the parachute reaches a steady 'terminal velocity' at which the forces of air resistance and gravity are balanced. On the Moon, where there is no atmosphere and hence no air resistance, the parachute would continue to accelerate until it hit the ground. Astronauts on the Moon do not use parachutes.

Answers
1. Plastic bag.
2. Paper towel.
3. Coloured paper and newspaper.
4. Plastic bag.
5. This parachute took the longest time to fall, and a parachute is meant to slow you down.
6. Any two factors such as: same size of parachute, same shape of parachute, same object hanging from parachute, all parachutes dropped from the same height, all parachutes held and dropped in the same way.
7. Any of the factors listed above could be investigated, or the children might think of others. Look for completion of the appropriate sections of the plan.

 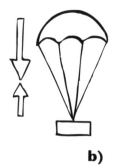 

a)   **b)**   **c)**

a) Closed parachute: gravity stronger than air resistance, the parachute accelerates.
b) Opening parachute: air resistance increases, reducing the acceleration.
c) Falling parachute: gravity and air resistance are balanced, so the parachute falls at a steady speed.

Parachutes

A group of children were testing parachutes to see how the material used to make the parachute affected the time it took to fall. They used a stopwatch to measure the times.

This is a graph of their results.

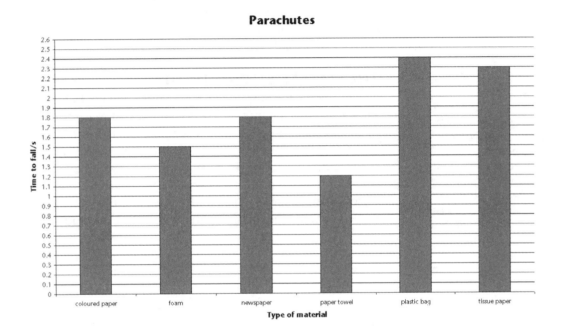

Questions

1. Which parachute took the longest time to fall?

2. Which parachute fell the fastest?

3. Which two parachutes took the same time to fall?

4. Which would be the best of these materials for a real parachute?

5. Explain your answer to Question 4.

6. Name two things the children should do to make the investigation fair.

7. Think of another feature of parachutes that the children could investigate. Write a full plan to show how they could carry out the investigation. Include the following:

- what to change each time
- what to measure each time
- what to keep the same each time
- a blank table for the results, showing the headings and units
- a blank graph for your results – label the axes correctly and give the units.

BOATS IN THE GUTTER

National Curriculum Science KS2 PoS Sc4: 2c
QCA Science Unit 4E: Friction
Scottish 5–14 Guidelines Forces and their effects – Levels C, D

HOW TO GATHER THE DATA

You can either buy a commercial kit to do this investigation or buy the components from a DIY shop. The shaped fronts of the boats can be made from card if cutting them from balsa wood is too slow. Masses of 100g or so and distances of 1–2m will give reasonable times that the children can measure. By Year 4/Primary 5, the children should be learning to use a stopwatch. Use one-second timers if their maths skills are less well developed.

THE SCIENCE BEHIND THE DATA

Gravity causes the suspended mass to pull the boat along, and the water resists this motion. Friction resisting movement through a fluid is called 'drag'. A more pointed shape has to push fewer water particles from its path at any one time. A broader shape has to push more particles from its path at any one time, so the water resistance is greater. Observing the 'bow wave' and 'wake' closely helps the children to understand that the water is being moved aside by the boat, and that this causes the drag.

Answers

1. Adnan's boat may be the most common answer, but make sure the children link this to their answer to Question 2.

2. This is the most pointed shape, the most streamlined shape or the shape with the least drag.

3. Any three from: same mass of boat, same material for boat (same grade of balsa wood), same mass hanging on keeper, same temperature of water, same string, same width of gutter, same depth of gutter (these last two are relevant because the gutter is quite narrow and the water is quite shallow).

4. Adnan's

5. Bethan's

6. It took the longest time (discourage answers referring to the height of the bar: the children need to give their answers in terms of data interpretation, not simple observation).

7. 12s

8. The prediction should be realistic and based on these results and the shape of the boat. A more pointed shape than Adnan's should take less time, but probably not less than 5 seconds. A wider boat should be slower. A dimpled shape can reduce drag because it creates small turbulences. These ideas can be discussed at different levels with different children. Encourage them to express their ideas coherently and concisely. This is a useful diagnostic tool, and can also be used to compare the children's ability to verbalise an idea to their ability to write an explanation.

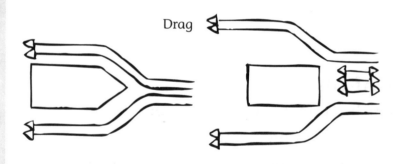

Drag

Another way of explaining this is to talk about the movement of the boat. As the boat moves through the water, it has momentum. Each time it collides with the water particles, the boat loses some of its own momentum to the water, so the boat travels less fast. With a broader shape, more water particles are moved at once, so momentum is lost more quickly and the boat travels more slowly. The children may also talk about streamlining – but beware of them just using the word and not being able to explain why a streamlined shape can move more quickly through water.

Boats in the gutter

Some children decided to investigate how different-shaped boats travel through water. They made boats from balsa wood. Each boat had a different shape:

Adnan's boat

Bethan's boat

Carly's boat

Darren's boat

They carried out an investigation by using weights to drag each boat through water in a length of gutter. They timed how long the boat took to get from one end to the other.

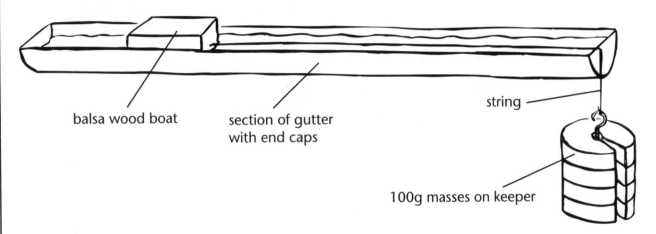

balsa wood boat

section of gutter with end caps

string

100g masses on keeper

Questions

1. Predict which boat will be the fastest.

2. Explain your prediction scientifically.

3. Name three things the children should have kept the same to make the investigation a fair test.

This is a graph of the children's results.

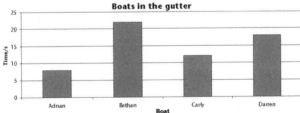

4. Which boat was actually the quickest? Use the graph to decide.

5. Which boat was the slowest?

6. How did you know that from the graph?

7. How long did it take for Carly's boat to travel along the gutter?

8. Draw a different shape for a boat and predict how long it will take to travel the same distance.

WHY IS SWIMMING DIFFICULT?

National Curriculum Science KS2 PoS Sc4: 2c
QCA Science Unit 4E: Friction
Scottish 5–14 Guidelines Forces and their effects – Level C

HOW TO GATHER THE DATA

It is too difficult to differentiate between the shapes if water is used in this investigation, as the times will vary only slightly. Wallpaper paste provides a liquid medium of greater viscosity (thickness), so it is easier to measure how well the different shapes move. You will need to experiment with the amount of wallpaper paste – 3 heaped teaspoons to 250cm³ of water is a rough guide. Use the largest clear plastic measuring cylinder you have (they can be bought from educational suppliers).

Children really enjoy this investigation. It gives them an opportunity to show creativity: the parachute (mushroom) and corkscrew shapes were suggested by children. Give the children about 25g of Plasticine each and ask them to roll and press it into a particular shape. They then have to predict (with a reason) whether the shape will take a short or long time to pass through the water.

THE SCIENCE BEHIND THE DATA

Most children have experienced how much more difficult it is to walk in water than in air – that when they are swimming (particularly underwater) they can feel the effort of pushing through the water. But they may not have thought about or tried to explain this scientifically. When they move through water they can see a wave made by the water they have pushed out of the way. They cannot see this effect with air, but they can feel it. When they move through water, a force called water resistance (which is similar to air resistance and friction) resists their movement. However, it also enables them to swim, because it gives them something to push against.

Discuss with the children how the body shapes they take up when swimming help them to move through the water. Watch videos or TV programmes about ocean life to observe how quickly most fish move through the water, and compare their own body shapes with the shapes of fish. Different species of fish have different shapes to suit their patterns of movement and feeding.

Encourage the children to draw diagrams with arrows to show the forces. This will be useful to support later work on opposing forces in Key Stage 2 and on balanced forces in Key Stage 3.

Answers

1. The torpedo shape.
2. It is long, thin and pointed, so the liquid can flow easily around the shape.
3. The parachute shape.
4. The liquid gets 'caught' under the curved top of the parachute and resists being moved aside.
5. 45 seconds
6. The cube shape.
7. 57 seconds
8. Water resistance, drag, or friction.
9. Divers stretch themselves so they are a thin, straight shape like a torpedo, because this is the best shape to help them hit the water and move through it without getting hurt.
10. Streamlined
11. The child should observe that the fish has a thin, streamlined shape. Some fish are flattened vertically to help them swim faster up and down. Other fish are flattened horizontally to help them swim easily along the sea bottom.
12. It is difficult for people to swim through water because their bodies are not very streamlined, so they experience a lot of water resistance when they try to move forward through water.

Why is swimming difficult?

Year 4 went swimming in the morning. They were telling their teacher how difficult it was to walk through the water and to swim underwater. Neil had noticed that was easier if he stretched and made a long narrow shape, like a fish.

The teacher set up an investigation for the children to test their ideas. She poured some liquid wallpaper paste into a large clear plastic tube. She gave all the children a small piece of Plasticine, approximately the same weight. The children had to make different shapes and test how quickly these fell through the paste. They recorded their results in a bar graph.

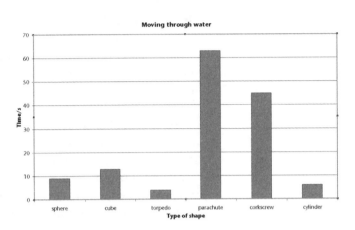

Questions

1. Which shape moved through the wallpaper paste the fastest?

2. Explain why this shape moved so well.

3. Which shape moved through the wallpaper paste most slowly?

4. Explain why this shape moved so slowly.

5. How long did the corkscrew take to move through the wallpaper paste?

6. Which shape took 13 seconds to fall through the wallpaper paste?

7. How much longer did it take for the parachute to fall through the wallpaper paste than the cylinder?

8. What is the name of the force that makes it harder for objects to move through water?

9. What shape do divers make before they enter the water from a high diving board? Explain why.

10. What word do we use for shapes that move through water and air easily?

11. Look at books and CD-ROMs for different shapes of fish. Choose a fish and decide whether you think it can move through water easily. Give your reasons. You could then model the shape of the fish and test it to find out whether your prediction was right.

12. Give a scientific explanation of why it is difficult for people to swim through water.

HANDLING SCIENCE DATA YEAR 4

STRIKE A LIGHT

National Curriculum Science KS2 PoS Sc3: 1c; Sc4: 1a, b
QCA Science Unit 4F: Circuits and conductors
Scottish 5–14 Guidelines Properties and uses of energy – Levels A, C;
Materials from Earth – Levels A, B

HOW TO GATHER THE DATA

This is a popular activity for children of all abilities, and can be used to test a wide range of different objects and materials. The children can use this type of circuit to test for broken wires and dead bulbs, and this can be used as an extension exercise for children who have finished the main activity.

THE SCIENCE BEHIND THE DATA

In general, metals conduct electricity and non-metals do not. Electrical effects are caused when electrons move through a material. All materials contain electrons, but not all materials conduct electricity. In metals, the electrons can move easily through the whole of the metal (they are called 'mobile electrons'). They can pass easily from one metal object to another one that is touching it – even when the two metals are of different types. The battery makes all the electrons in the metal move in the same direction at the same time, resulting in a flow of electricity (a current). A rope circuit can be used to model this idea. The electrons actually move quite slowly, but because all the electrons move at once the effect is instantaneous.

Non-metals (except graphite, see below) do not have mobile electrons. In non-metals, however, some of the electrons can move within the material and build up an area of charge. This can be made to happen by rubbing the material, which produces the effect of static electricity. Electrons move to one part of the material, collecting together to make an area of negative charge which can be attracted to positive charges in another surface, so the two surfaces stick together.

Graphite, which is used in pencil 'leads' and electrical motors, is the only solid non-metal that contains mobile electrons and is thus a conductor.

The flow of electrons in a circuit is actually from the negative terminal to the positive – but historically, electricity has been described as flowing from positive to negative. The latter direction is referred to as the direction of *conventional current*. The children could use either convention to describe electrical flow; but I prefer to think of the flow of electrons, and thus of electricity going from the negative terminal to the positive. This also fits better with ideas in chemistry at Key Stages 3 and 4.

Answers

1. Circuit 3.
2. Tick: magnet, steel spanner, gold ring, steel knife. Cross: football, wax crayons, wooden chair, book, plastic ruler.
3.

Metallic	Non-metallic
Magnet	Football
Steel spanner	Wooden chair
Gold ring	Plastic ruler
Steel knife	Wax crayons
	Book

4.

Conductor	Insulator
Magnet	Football
Steel spanner	Wax crayons
Gold ring	Wooden chair
Steel knife	Book
	Plastic ruler

5. The two wires meant to link through the material being tested are touching anyway, so there is a complete circuit without the electricity having to pass through the material.

Strike a light

Class 4 knew that a bulb can light up when wires are used to make connections in a circuit. They wanted to find out whether other materials could be used as well.

Questions

1. Which circuit should they use for their investigation?

1.

3.

2. Put a tick or a cross against each of these objects to say whether the bulb would light if the object were used in your circuit.

Metallic	Non-metallic

3. Complete the first table on the right to group the materials these objects are made from as metallic or non-metallic.

Conductor	Insulator

4. Complete the second table to group the same materials as electrical conductors or insulators.

5. Jack connected his circuit as shown on the right. The bulb lit up every time. Why do you think that happened?

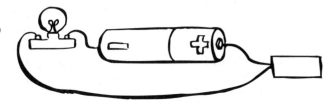

ADDING BATTERIES

National Curriculum Science KS2 PoS Sc4: 1a, b
QCA Science Unit 4F: Circuits and conductors
Scottish 5–14 Guidelines Properties and uses of energy – Levels C, D;
Conversion and transfer of energy – Level C

HOW TO GATHER THE DATA

This investigation uses a datalogger and light sensor to gather evidence that supports a general observation. It can be carried out by one or two children, perhaps as part of a circus of activities. For this type of datalogger the actual shape of the graph is more or less linear at the lower values, but tends to a curve at the higher values (this change has been ignored in the graph shown). The investigation will also show that similar-looking bulbs are not identical in brightness. Also, if the batteries are nearly spent you will not get reliable results.

THE SCIENCE BEHIND THE DATA

An appropriate explanation for this age level follows. The batteries 'push' the electricity, which carries energy around the circuit. The release of energy makes the bulb glow as electricity passes through it. The more batteries you have, the harder the electricity is pushed: more electricity goes around the circuit, more energy is released, and the bulb becomes hotter and brighter.

A fuller explanation follows (some of this could be explored with Year 6 children, using suitable investigations to provide evidence). The amount of 'push' in a circuit is measured in volts. It depends on the type and number of batteries. (We are using the terms 'battery' and 'bulb' in their most familiar senses. However, strictly speaking, the common 1.5V 'battery' is a cell, and a battery is a collection of cells. A 9V battery contains six 1.5V cells. The correct electrical term for a 'bulb' is a lamp.) The flow of electricity around a circuit is really the flow of electrons (negatively charged particles from the metal atoms). A chemical reaction within the battery releases electrons with higher energy, and as these flow some of the energy is transferred to the surroundings – so heat is generated. The electrons returning to the battery have less energy than those being released.

When electricity is passing through a component, there is some resistance to its flow (the thinner the wire, the greater the resistance). The greater the resistance of a component, the more quickly energy is lost at that point. The brightness of a bulb depends upon the resistance of the filament wire and the amount of electricity passing through it. If the resistance is high, a lot of the energy is lost quickly and the bulb shines very brightly. The light and heat transfer energy from the circuit to the surroundings. More batteries can 'push' more electricity around the circuit, so energy can be transferred more quickly. If the filament gets too hot, it breaks and the bulb 'blows'. When the battery 'runs out', it is the energy that 'runs out', not the electricity. The chemicals releasing the high-energy electrons have been used up, so the battery cannot 'push' any more. In a rechargeable battery, the chemicals can be reformed by 'pushing' electricity in the opposite direction.

Answers

1. One battery.
2. Yes.
3. The brightness increases as the number of batteries increases.
4. With more batteries, there is more electricity going round the circuit. Discourage the use of the word *power*, which is not appropriate in this context. The child could say that more batteries give a greater 'push' to the electricity.
5. To make sure that the light sensor would only measure the light from the bulb, not any of the light in the room.
6. A bar to 90%.
7. The brightness goes up by 5% with each new battery, so the next one should be 90%.
8. Positive and negative. They tell you which way round to connect the battery.

Adding batteries

Mark said that if you put more batteries in a circuit, the bulb will be brighter. Anna and her friend Heather investigated this. They set up a circuit to make a bulb light using one battery. Then they used two batteries. The bulb seemed brighter.

"How can we measure how bright the bulbs are?"

"We could use a datalogger with a light sensor."

They set up their circuit with a light sensor above the bulb, then put a black tube around the bulb and the sensor. They drew a diagram of their circuit.

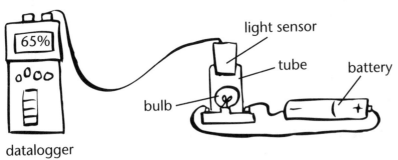

This is a bar graph of the children's results.

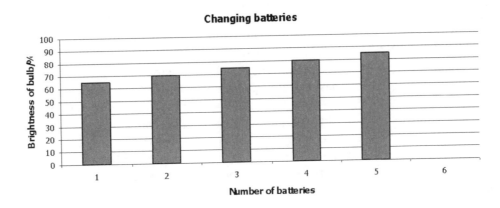

Questions

1. Look at the reading on the datalogger in the picture. How many batteries give that brightness?

2. Mark said that the more batteries they used, the brighter the bulb would be. Did the investigation show that was true?

3. How did you tell that from the graph?

4. Why do you think the brightness changes when you use more batteries?

5. Why did the children put a black tube around the light sensor?

6. Predict the brightness for 6 batteries. Draw a bar on the graph to show it.

7. Explain your prediction.

8. What do the two signs on the ends of a battery mean? How do they help you?

ADDING BULBS

National Curriculum Science KS2 PoS Sc4: 1a, b
QCA Science Unit 4F: Circuits and conductors
Scottish 5–14 Guidelines Properties and uses of energy – Levels C, D;
Conversion and transfer of energy – Level C

HOW TO GATHER THE DATA

The effect of changing the number of bulbs in a circuit can be judged by direct observation, but to measure the change in the current you will need an ammeter (or you could use a datalogger, as in 'Adding batteries' on page 58). Ammeters are uncommon in primary schools, but you may be able to borrow one from a local secondary school (they cost about £30). Using an ammeter will demonstrate that the current is not 'used up' when a bulb is lit – many children and adults think this. You can show that the current on either side of the bulb is exactly the same. It is important for this activity to use bulbs of the same age and type, so that they have the same brightness.

THE SCIENCE BEHIND THE DATA

An appropriate explanation for this age level follows. The more bulbs there are in the circuit, the harder it is for the electricity to flow through, so the electric current (shown by the ammeter reading) is reduced.

A fuller explanation follows (this could be explored with Year 6 children, using suitable investigations to provide evidence). The flow of electricity is really the flow of electrons (negatively charged particles from the metal atoms) around the circuit. When electricity is passing through any component, there is always some resistance to its flow. The copper wires often used for circuits in schools have a very low resistance, because (a) copper is a very good conductor of electricity and (b) the wires are thick (the thinner the wire, the higher the resistance). The filament in a bulb is a very fine wire of a higher-resistance metal, so a bulb has a significant effect on the flow of electricity.

The battery can be considered as the component that 'pushes' the electricity around the circuit (the amount of 'push' is called the 'voltage' of the battery). If the resistance is high, it is more difficult for the battery to push the electrons around, so less electricity will flow (this is measured as the 'current'). If a second bulb is put in the circuit, this will virtually double the resistance, so even less electricity (half as much) will flow. Each time a bulb is added, the total resistance is increased and so less current flows.

There is a formula to describe this, called 'Ohm's Law': voltage = current × resistance. If you keep the voltage from the battery constant and double the resistance, you will halve the current.

Answers

1. 3 bulbs.

2. The greater the number of bulbs, the smaller the amount of electricity that flows in the circuit. (Encourage the children to state both what factor is being changed and what effect this produces.)

3. The bars decrease in size as the number of bulbs increases, so less electricity is flowing.

4. They will be dimmer. (Look for a logical explanation in the answer to Question 5.)

5. There will be less electricity flowing in the circuit, so the bulbs will not be as bright.

6. A bar in between 0.4 amps and 0.7 amps, close to 0.5 amps.

7.

Number of bulbs	Amount of electricity/amps
1	2.0
2	1.0
3	0.7
4	0.5
5	0.4
6	0.3

8. The amount of electricity would be twice as great.

9. The battery pushes the electricity around the circuit, so two batteries can push more electricity through the bulbs than one.

Adding bulbs

Matthew and Daniel tried putting more bulbs in a circuit to see what would happen. The bulbs became dimmer. They wanted to find out why. Their teacher lent them a meter (ammeter) to measure how much electricity was going around the circuit.

This is how they set up the circuit.

Here is a bar graph of their results, with one result missing.

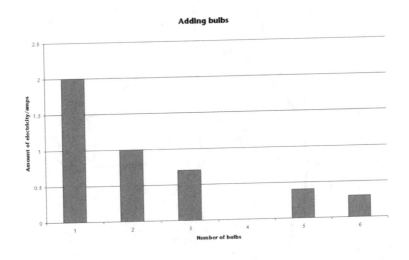

Questions

1. Look at the reading on the meter in the picture. Use the graph to find out how many bulbs are connected in the circuit to give this reading. Ignore the number of bulbs drawn in the picture.

2. How does the number of bulbs affect the amount of electricity in the circuit?

3. How did you decide this from the graph?

4. If more than 6 bulbs are used, do you think they will be brighter or dimmer than before (or stay the same)?

5. Give a reason for your answer to Question 4.

6. Draw the missing bar for 4 bulbs in the circuit.

7. Design a table the children could have used to record their results in. Write in the table what you think the reading was for each test.

8. What would happen to the amount of electricity if two batteries were used instead of one?

9. Explain your answer to Question 8.

HANDLING SCIENCE DATA YEAR 4

Pond life jigsaw

shows direction of food (energy)

Great diving beetle

Water louse

Water flea

Lesser water boatman

Dead matter

Microscopic plants

Pond weed

Small pond snail

Stickleback

Algae

Tadpole

Newt

HANDLING SCIENCE DATA YEAR 4

Growing up

How tall am I ?

Height/cm

180
160
140
120
110
100
80
60
40
20
0

baby   toddler   teenager   adult

HANDLING SCIENCE DATA YEAR 4

Graph axes

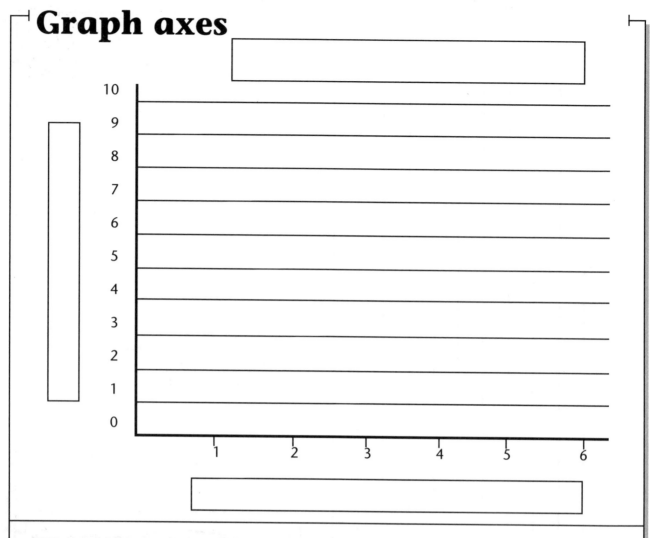

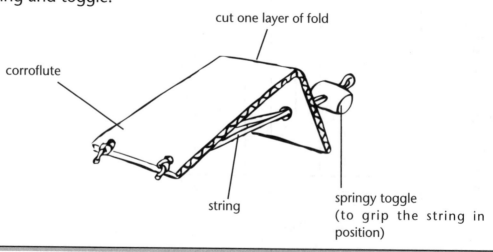

How to make a ramp

You can make a cheap, adjustable ramp for toy cars (see 'Car ramps', page 45) using corrugated plastic or 'corroflute'.

1. Take a length of corroflute and use a craft knife to cut through **one** surface (along a corrugation, not across) so that it hinges.
2. Use a hole punch to make holes as shown below.
3. Attach a string and toggle.

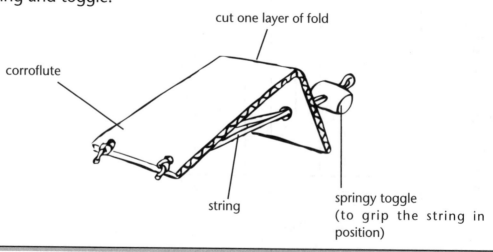

cut one layer of fold

corroflute

string

springy toggle
(to grip the string in
position)